Henry Ford Community College | Biology 233

Human Anatomy & Physiology 1
Lecture Guide

Third Edition

Krol | Vining | Palaski

http://sciweb.hfcc.net

PEARSON

Custom
Publishing

Printed in the United States of America

20 19 18 17 16 15 14 13 12

ISBN 0-536-49744-3

2007140369

MW

Please visit our web site at *www.pearsoncustom.com*

PEARSON CUSTOM PUBLISHING
501 Boylston Street, Suite 900, Boston, MA 02116
A Pearson Education Company

PREFACE

To You, Our Student:

As you choose a career and pursue such, it becomes apparent that so much must be learned before graduating into that field. This is true especially for the sciences. The sciences have exploded in information within the past two decades making the attainment of a career goal more difficult. Biology and medicine have led the way in this information explosion. Also, with all the costs of living including tuition increases, more of you are working to support the goal of a career. This reduces your time available for learning and increases the stress level and confusion. Making good use of your time or good time management becomes very important. This is one of the primary objectives of this book.

This study guide for Biology 233-*Anatomy and Physiology I* will specify and thus narrow the information and concepts you need to learn. By identifying that which is to be learned and presenting it in an organized manner becomes the second objective of this package I have organized for you.

The **Lecture Guide** book you are holding is organized first, by the chapters covered in this course. Each chapter starts with a CHAPTER OVERVIEW. Then chapter objectives are identified. This list will state the overall objectives for the chapter. These are the core or basic concepts to be learned as your study each chapter. The SUMMARY section relates some basic concepts on the chapter's topic. Toward the end of each unit are PRACTICE STUDY QUESTIONS for your review. Attempt to answer these and check your answers with the answer page that follows. Your expectations from this course and from your instructor should be unlike any course you have experienced in college. What we in anatomy and physiology teach and what you learn become accountable to many other individuals, courses, programs and of course your careers. Your responsibility is to take from this book, your course and instructor all that you can as you learn to understand the information and concepts presented in class. This LECTURE GUIDE book is designed to make that goal more achievable. Achieving this takes time and a commitment to the course.

It is our sincerest hope that all students who use this **LECTURE GUIDE** book will consider it a valuable and an enjoyable contribution to their learning experiences of human anatomy and physiology.

E. J. Krol, Ph.D.,   Mr. Stewart Vining, M.S.,   Mr. Michael Palaski, M.S.

P.S. Learning should be an ongoing experience throughout your life. Every person you encounter, good, bad or indifferent should teach you something about yourself and others. This will improve your outlook on life. The rewards will be a personal growth and positive perspective of yourself. Thus, living involves a commitment to the pursuit of life-long learning. This is especially true if you are going to be the best at whatever you attempt and endeavor both in your chosen career and personal life.

ACKNOWLEDGMENTS

Years ago (early 1980's) each of these chapters was printed by HFCC Graphic Arts and distributed free to the students with many errors and incomplete ideas and explanations. Those packages stacked over 47 feet (by one student's calculations) in my office and cluttered the office every semester; besides its regular disorganization. However thanks to a Macintosh computer, a desktop publishing program and a laser printer this package you hold came into existence. I would like to express my appreciation to many past and present students for offering organization and content suggestions for this type of book over the past years. Specifically: Laurie Juozunas, Lynn Kapulak, Connie Inman, Janet Russ, Dawn Hynds, Jim Follbaum, Corey Osborne, Wendy Hiltunen, Carol Emerson, Susan Blaesser, Jim Herman, Ruth Kaminski, Lyn Holtmeyer, Debbie Riley, Theresa Bently, Marc Sargis, Brad Kostrzewa, Vicki Kramer, Michelle Downham, Sherry Wilson, Yalonda Peete, Mary Twombly, Yalonda Peete, Clinton McDade, Ilonka Toporan, Steve Carr and Lisa Meyer have offered content, corrections and encouragement toward this package. However, many others who have been unintentionally forgotten or overlooked in this short list offered help with many ideas.

Many instructors at Henry Ford Community College from the Biology, Nursing, Respiratory Therapy, Physical therapist, and Surgical technologist programs have over many years offered constant suggestions, changes, additions and corrections toward this study package. Some of those individuals are now retired while many current instructors both full time and part time continue to offer their ideas and needs.

I along with the co-authors intend to revise this package for every printing and thus would appreciate ideas to improve its organization and content. If you have any ideas, let's talk. Your name, of course, would become part of the current list.

Dr. E. J. Krol, Ph. D.

Table Of Contents

List of Figures, Tables, Charts

An Introduction to Anatomy and Physiology

Overview

This first chapter presents an analysis of the meanings of anatomy and physiology and the interrelationship between structure and function. The unit begins with the five structural levels of organization that comprise the body--chemicals, cells, tissues, organs, and the systems--and the general functions of these principal body systems are described. The structural plan of the entire body is then described. Among other topics considered are the location and contents of the principal body cavities, the characteristics of the anatomical position, the association of anatomical terms with common names of body regions, the use of directional terms, planes of the body, and how sections of the body are made. Comparisons or relationships are also made between radiographic anatomy, CTs MRIs and the diagnosis of the disease. The chapter then places considerable emphasis on the meaning of stress and homeostasis, the interrelationships of body systems in maintaining homeostasis, and the role of the endocrine and nervous systems in controlling homeostasis. The feedback system is defined using the regulation of blood pressure and blood sugar level as examples.

Chapter Objectives

1. Describe the basic functions of organisms.
2. Define anatomy and physiology, and describe various specialties of each discipline.
3. Identify the major levels of organization in organisms, from the simplest to the most complex.
4. Identify the organ systems of the human body and the major components of each system.
5. Explain the concept of homeostasis and its significance for living and survival.
6. Describe how positive feedback and negative feedback are involved in homeostatic regulation.
7. Use anatomical terms to describe body sections, body regions, and relative positions.
8. Identify the major body cavities and their subdivisions.

Concepts and definitions

1.   Through a study of anatomy and its subdivisions, the body may be examined at different levels of structural organization.
2.   Anatomy is generally defined as the study of structure or the naming of structures.
3.   Physiology explains the function of body parts; the structure of a part determines and limits its function.
4.   The levels of structural organization that comprise the body are chemicals, cells, tissues, organs, and systems.
5. Each body system is designed to perform definite functions, all of which contribute to homeostasis.
6.   The human body separated by the spine has bilateral symmetry, and a tube-within-a-tube organization. Directional terms are used to precisely locate one part of the body relative to another.

7. Body spaces containing <u>viscera</u> are called cavities. The principal cavities include the dorsal (cranial and vertebral) and ventral (thoracic, abdominal, and pelvic).

8. Obvious bony, muscular, vascular and nervous structures may be located on the body surface and used to locate or position other organs.

9. Common names for <u>regions</u> of the body also have anatomical names. Examples are the cranium (skull), brachium (arm), cervical (neck), and plantar (sole).

10. Specific terms describe the location of structures on or in the body. They are applied when the body is in anatomical position.

11. In the anatomical position, the body is erect, facing forward, the arms are at the sides, and the palms of the hands are facing forward.

12. The structural plan of the body is also understood by passing <u>planes</u> through it. Such planes include the sagittal, frontal, and horizontal (or axial). The use of cross, oblique, an longitudinal sections helps to understand the relationship of various parts of the body to each other.

13. A very specialized branch of anatomy that is essential for the diagnosis of many disorders is radiographic anatomy, which includes the use of x-rays.

14. An x-ray technique called CAT (computed axial tomography) scanning combines the principals of both x-ray and advanced computer technology.

15. <u>Homeostasis</u> is the maintenance of a relatively constant internal environment. The maintenance of homeostasis results in health; physiological imbalance without homeostasis to bring it back to normal will result in disease.

16. A stressor is any stimulus that attempts to disrupt homeostasis.

17. Stress is the body's response to a stressor. The changes in body functions are not noticed immediately.

18. Homeostasis is controlled by the endocrine and nervous systems, and is usually achieved through the function of negative feedback systems.

19. Various types of measurements are important in understanding the human body.

Summary

Assuming the body is in anatomical position, the terms of direction convey information as to the location of body structures relative to one another. These terms are also used in the names of many specific organs and their parts. For example, the vena cava (returning blood to the right atrium of the heart) are divided into the *superior* and *inferior* vena cava and there are internal, middle, and external layers of tissue in these vessel walls.

Studying the body and its organs by making cuts or planes of section in various directions supplies further information as to orientation and location of components. Sections are particularly useful in studying the microscopic anatomy (histology) of the body. Certain planes are also utilized in the naming of specific body features; for example, the superior sagittal sinus (a blood vessel in the mid-line of the brain); or coronal suture (a joint running from side to side over the top of the skull).

Male and female bodies differ in prominence of muscular, bony, and vascular structures and in angularity. Because of a thicker layer of fat tissue beneath the skin, the female body is typically more rounded and softer in appearance than the male.

Infants also usually have thicker fat layers and skin than older children. Older adults have less elasticity to their skin and less muscle tone, so that body outlines may be altered. In any individual, gross body areas establish regions within which specific anatomical landmarks and reference points may be located.

Summary Outline

Biological Sciences study's life and its normal functions. Science is organized or classified knowledge. Medicine draws on biology and is the science and art that studies diseases and their cures.

I. Anatomy
   A. Macroscopic structure, gross anatomy
      An ancient science
         Hippocrates - 460 to 357 BC, "father of medicine"
         Aristotle - 384 to 322 BC
         Galen - 129-199 AD Greek physician, writer
         Andreaus Vesalius - AD 1514 to 1564, Belgium anatomist ;
         Albinus - 1697-1770, German anatomist
         Leonardo DaVinci - 1452 to 1519, anatomical artist, sculptor
   B. Microscopic structure
      Histology-study of tissues
      Cytology-study of cells
   C. Morphology, or Structure
      Embryology, early growth and development
    Comparative anatomy   Study of similarities and differences among various species of animals
      Comparative embryology
      Pathology, abnormal anatomy, both macroscopic and microscopic

II. Body Cavities
   A. Ventral cavity (anterior cavity)
      1. Thoracic cavity
         Two pleural membranes (parietal pleura and visceral pleura)
         Mediastinum
      Contents: esophagus, trachea, lungs, heart, blood and lymph vessels, thymus gland, nerves
         Diaphragm-separates thoracic and abdomenopelvic cavity
      2. Abdomenopelvic cavity
         Abdominal cavity
         Peritoneal cavity
      Contents: stomach, spleen, pancreas, liver, gallbladder, kidneys, small and large intestines
         Pelvic cavity
            Contents: bladder, rectum, uterus, and prostate gland
   B. Dorsal cavity (posterior cavity)
      Cranial cavity - contains brain
      Spinal cavity (spinal canal) - contains spinal cord
   C. Facial Aspect of Skull
      Orbital cavities
         Eyes, optic nerves, muscles of the eyeballs, lacrimal apparatus
      Nasal cavity-structures forming the nose
      Buccal Cavity
         Tongue, teeth, salivary glands

III. Anatomical Position and directional terms

Dorsal vs. Ventral	Superior vs. Inferior	Anterior vs. Posterior
Medial vs. Lateral	Cranial vs. Caudal	Proximal vs. Distal

IV. Anatomical planes

Sagittal and mid-sagittal plane
Coronal (frontal) plane
Transverse (trans axial) plane
Horizontal (axial) plane

V. Overall Organization

A. **C e l l .** The basic unit or functional unit of life

B. **T i s s u e .** A group of cells with similar structure and function

C. **O r g a n .** A physiologic unit composed of two or more tissues that together perform a special function

D. **S y s t e m .** An arrangement of organs closely allied and concerned with the same function. Systems found in the human body:

Skeletal	Endocrine Muscular	Respiratory Nervous
Digestive	Vascular, or Circulatory	Lymphatic
Excretory	Reproductive	

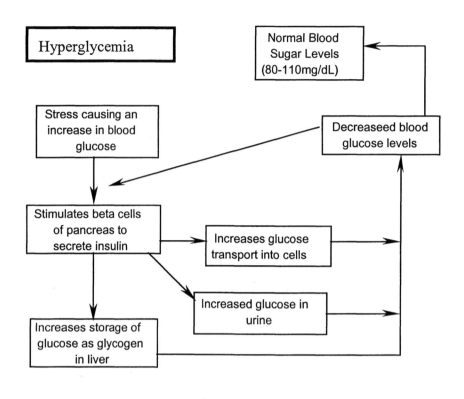

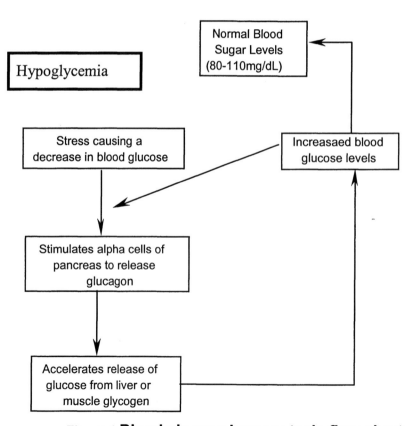

Figure 1 Blood glucose homeostasis flow chart

Practice Test Questions

Matching

1. Anterior/Ventral	_10_	a. Above; higher on body than reference point
2. Deep	_5_	b. Outside of
3. Distal	_4_	c. Back of the body
4. Posterior/dorsal	_2_	d. Closer to the center line
5. External	_12_	e. Closer to the surface
6. Inferior	_1_	f. Belly side or front of body
7. Internal	_7_	g. Inside
8. Lateral	_6_	h. Below; lower on body than reference point
9. Medial	_3_	i. Further from attachment point
10. Superior	_j_	j. Further from the surface
11. Proximal	_8_	k. To the side
12. Superficial	_11_	l. Closest to attachment point
13. Midsagittal/median plane	_14_	m. Parallel to median plane
14. Parasagittal plane	_16_	n. Divides body into superior and inferior parts
15. Coronal/frontal plane	_15_	o. Divides body into front and back halves
16. Axial or horizontal plane	_13_	p. Divides body into equal lateral halves
17. Longitudinal section	_18_	q. Cuts across organ's shortest dimension
18. Cross-section	_19_	r. Infant's soft spot; closes at about one year
19. Anterior fontanel	_17_	s. Parallels organ's longest dimension

Multiple Choice

1. The cranium contours are determined by:
   - a. the muscles
   - b. the brain
   - c. the bony structures
   - d. the soft spots

2. The facial contours are determined by:
   - a. the fleshy and muscular parts
   - b. the bony structure
   - c. the shape of the mouth
   - d. the size of the chin

Completion

1. In the anatomical position the body is _____, the eyes are _____, the arms are _____ with the palms _____ and the feet _____ with heels _____.

2. The premature infant lacks the subcutaneous layer of _____ found in the full term infant.

3. The female accumulates fat pads at the time of _____.

4. In old age the skin hangs loosely, as in the premature, but is due to _____.

5. The female posture is less erect because _____.

6. Label the following abdominal quadrants and areas within your sketch.

7. Identify the location of the following organs:

	Quadrant	Region
a. stomach	_____	_____
b. liver	_____	_____
c. right kidney	_____	_____
d. left ovary	_____	_____
e. spleen	_____	_____
f. gall bladder	_____	_____
g. rectum	_____	_____
h. cecum	_____	_____

ANSWERS

Matching

1. f 2. j 3. i 4. c 5. b 6. h 7. g 8. k 9. d 10. a
11. l 12. e 13. p 14. m 15. o 16. n 17. s 18. q 19. r

Multiple Choice

1. c 2. a

Completion

1. Standing erect, level and looking straight ahead, at the sides, forward, parallel, approximated.
2. adipose tissue
3. puberty
4. loss of elasticity and disappearance of fat
5. a more pronounced curvature of the lower back [thoracic curve]
6. a. right upper quadrant (RUQ)
   b. left upper quadrant (LUQ)
   c. right lower quadrant (RLQ)
   d. left lower quadrant (LLQ)
   e. right hypochondriac area
   f. epigastric area
   g. left hypochondriac area
   h. right lumbar area
   i. Umbilical area
   j. Left lumbar area
   k. right iliac area
   l. hypogastric area
   m. Left iliac area

7. a. LUQ, epigastric
   b. RUQ, epigastric, Right and Left Hypochondriac
   c. RUQ, Right Lumbar
   d. LLQ, left inguinal
   e. LUQ, left hypochondriac
   f. RUQ, right hypochondriac
   g. LLQ, hypogastric
   h. RLQ, right lumbar

The Chemical Level of Organization

Overview

This unit provides the essential background of chemistry needed to understand the physiology of the body. Among the topics considered are chemical elements, atomic structure, molecule formation, ionic and covalent bonding, radioactive tracers, and chemical reactions. The structure and importance of the inorganic substances--water, acids, bases, and salts--are emphasized. The structure and importance of the organic substances described include carbohydrates, lipids, proteins, nucleic acids, ATP, cyclic AMP, and prostaglandins. The concept of pH and the role of buffer systems in maintaining homeostasis are also analyzed.

Chapter Objectives

1. Describe an atom and how atomic structure affects interactions between atoms.
2. Compare the ways in which atoms combine to form molecules and compounds.
3. Use chemical notation to symbolize chemical reactions.
4. Distinguish among the major types of chemical reactions that are important for studying physiology.
5. Describe the crucial role of enzymes in metabolism.
6. Distinguish between organic and inorganic compounds.
7. Explain how the chemical properties of water make life possible.
8. Discuss the importance of pH and the role of buffers in body fluids.
9. Describe the physiological roles of inorganic compounds.
10. Discuss the structures and functions of carbohydrates, lipids, proteins, nucleic acids, and high-
     energy compounds.

Concepts and definitions

1.   The human body is a collection of molecules composed of atoms; the most abundant atoms within these molecules are carbon, hydrogen, oxygen, and nitrogen.
2.   Atoms combine to form molecules by bonding thus completing their outer orbital energy levels.
3.   A <u>covalent</u> <u>bond</u>, is a <u>sharing</u> of electrons between two atoms of a molecule. This continuous sharing bond contains energy and can only be broken by an enzyme and water.
4.   An <u>ionic</u> <u>bond</u> occurs when one or more <u>electrons leave</u> one atom and move over to another atom within the same molecule. These bonds are extremely weak and do not require enzymes to break them. Water will break these bonds.
5.   Radioisotopes emit radiation that can be detected by instruments. These isotopes are used in nuclear medicine to detect diseases in cell chemistry and structure.
6.   Chemical reactions involve BOTH the formation and breaking of chemical bonds. This causes atoms to exchange places between molecules thus forming new molecules or destroying other molecules.
7.   Water functions as a)solvent, b)suspending medium, c)heat absorber, and d)lubricant.
8.   An **acid** is a chemical or fluid that has the ability to release H^+ (proton).
9.   A **base** is a chemical or fluid that has the ability to absorb H^+ from a solution. Two common alkaline (base) anions are OH^- (hydroxyl ion) and the HCO_3^- (bicarbonate ion).
10.   Acids dissociate into H^+ that lower pH; bases dissociate into OH^- ions that raise pH.

11. Salts from our foods provide cations and anions that are required to maintain life's metabolic reactions.
12. pH is the measurement of the H^+ concentration within a fluid.
13. pH number is the degree of acidity or alkalinity of a fluid or solution.
14. pH is maintained by buffer systems.
15. A buffer is a chemical that maintains a pH. Acid buffers release H^+ and alkaline buffers absorb H^+.
16. Buffers are molecules that stabilize or protect a pH. The most active are the HCO_3^- ions. Other buffers include hemoglobin and phosphates.
17. The two major organ systems that regulate the pH in all fluid compartments are the lungs of the respiratory and kidneys of the urinary systems.
18. Carbohydrate use is the body's most immediate source of energy.
19. Lipids function in protection, insulation, storage, and in the synthesis of vitamins and hormones.
20. Proteins are used by the body to build, grow and repair tissues.
21. Proteins that function as enzymes (catalysts) regulate biochemical reactions.
22. DNA when functioning as a unit (gene) controls the activities of cells and stores hereditary information.
23. RNA assumes a significant role in protein synthesis.
24. ATP represents the body's energy-storage molecule.
25. Cyclic AMP is closely related to ATP and functions in certain hormonal reactions.
25. Prostaglandins are lipids that control the production of cyclic AMP, and mimic the effects of hormones.
26. Other functions of prostaglandins include regulating blood pressure, inducing labor, transmitting nerve impulses, regulating metabolism, and regulating muscular contractions of the gastrointestinal tract.

Summary Outline

All living and nonliving things consist of **matter**.

Matter -   Anything that has weight (mass) and occupies space.
                May exist in a solid, liquid or gaseous state.
                All matter (living and nonliving) is composed of substances called elements.

Element   -pure substance that can **not** be broken down into simpler substances.
       -111 different kinds of elements (92 naturally occurring)some made in laboratory.
       -Every element has a **name** and a **chemical symbol**
       -Over **90%** of the human body is composed of **3** elements (**C**arbon, **O**xygen, **H**ydrogen).
               only about **24** can be found in the body

Atom - smallest unit of an element.
       - smallest unit to enter into chemical reactions.
       Structure (if you cut away an atom you would see it is composed mainly of empty space).
       -In the center, there is an nucleus which contains subatomic particles called **neutrons** and
               protons.
       - Surrounding the nucleus you find particles called **electrons** orbiting the nucleus at different
               distances (**shells**) from the nucleus.

       - Atoms of different elements differ in size, weight number of subatomic particles and how they interact
               with other atoms
          - **Atomic number** - is the total number of protons in an atom.
               -The atomic number is different for every element.
          - **Atomic weight** - is the sum of the protons plus the neutrons in an atom.(neutrons = atomic
               weight - atomic number
       -If the number of **electrons** = **protons** in an atom we say the atom is **electrically neutral.**
          (atomic number = protons = electrons)
          -    electrons orbit around the nucleus at different distances from the nucleus **energy levels**
               (shells)

- **1st shell** - contains a maximum of 2 electrons
- **2nd shell** - contains a maximum of 8 electrons
- **3rd shell** - contains a maximum of 8 electrons
- **Ion** - a charged atom
    <u>Positively charged ion</u>- the number of electrons is less than the number of protons.
    <u>Negatively charged ion</u>- the number of electrons is greater than the number of protons.
- Ions are very <u>reactive</u> atoms and are involved in chemical <u>reactions</u>.

The atomic number (#of protons) of an atom or element is constant and never changes. This is not always the case for the atomic weight.

- **Isotope** - Atoms which have the same atomic number but different atomic weights.
    - Since the number of protons does not change for a given atom, <u>isotopes</u> must <u>vary</u> in the number of <u>neutrons</u>.
- read the textbook about unstable radioactive isotope tracing in medicine.

Compounds and Molecule

Compound - result of the combining of two or more different atoms.

Molecule - smallest part of a compound that still retains the properties of that compound.
- may form from two or more of the same atoms combine.
    (ex. O_2, H_2, N_2)

Reactions between Atoms

- Reactions between atoms to form molecules and compounds involve the electrons in the outer shell (valence electrons).
- Atoms are most <u>stable</u> when their <u>outer shell</u> is <u>complete</u> (full).

<u>Types of Reactions</u>

1. **Ionic Reaction** - molecules result from the transfer of electrons between atoms
    - ions of opposite charge are produced, and are attracted to each, forming molecules, This association is known as an **ionic bond.**
    - example (formation of sodium chloride)

2. **Covalent Reaction** - molecule results from the sharing of electrons between atoms so as to complete their outer shell.**(covalent bond)**
    - example (formation of water molecule)
    Types:
    1. <u>non-polar covalent bond</u> - Electrons are shared evenly between the two atoms involved.

    2. <u>polar covalent bond</u> - Electrons spend more time encircling one atom. (Ex. Water)

3. <u>hydrogen bond</u> - when a partially positive hydrogen is attracted to a partially negative atom in another molecule. (Ex. Water)

Types of Chemical Reactions
1. Synthesis Reactions   A + B -----> AB
2. Decomposition Reaction   AB -----> A + B
3. Exchange Reaction   AB + CD ----> AD + CB
4. Reversible Reaction   A + B <----> AB

Acids and Bases
Electrolytes - substances that release ions when dissolved in water
  Acids - substances that release hydrogen ions when they dissociate (break apart).
   - increases the hydrogen ion concentration of a solution. - Example. HCL
  Bases- substances that absorb H^+ or bind up H^+.
   - substances that release hydroxide ions when they dissociate.
   - increase the hydroxide ion concentration of a substance. Ex. NaOH
  Salt - electrolytes formed from the interaction of an acid and a base

pH Scale
- a way of measuring the hydrogen ion (H^+)concentrations of a substance.
- scale from 0 to 14.
- pure or distilled water pH = 7
- <u>Acids</u>; pH 0 to 7, Lower the pH number the greater the H^+ concentration.
- <u>Bases</u>; pH 7 to 14, Higher the pH number the greater the OH^- concentration.

There is a **10 fold increase** between each whole number on the pH scale.

Buffers - a chemical or combination of chemicals that takes up excess H^+ or OH^-.
- If you add an acid or base to a buffered solution the pH will only change slightly.
- Ex. **Buffered Aspirin**

Inorganic vs. Organic Compounds
- although inorganic compounds are associated with the non-living they are needed for proper functioning of the body.
- **Organic Chemistry** - Chemistry of Carbon

Carbon - is the most common element in the body.
  - a carbon atom has the unique property of being able to <u>share</u> <u>electrons</u> with up to <u>four</u> different atoms.
  - carbon atoms can share electrons with each other to form <u>rings</u> and <u>chains</u>.(carbon chain, ring)

Important Classes of Organic Compounds of Life

All are large **macromolecules** consisting of repeating **unit molecules**.

Macromolecules are produced by **Dehydration Synthesis** and broken down by the process of **Hydrolysis**

Macromolecules	Unit Molecule
1. **Proteins**	Amino acids
2. **Carbohydrates**	Monosaccharides
3. **Lipids**	Fatty Acids
4. **Nucleic Acids**	Nucleotides

1. Proteins

- very large molecules made up of smaller unit molecules called **amino acids**.
- **20** different amino acids found in the body.
- We can not produce **9 (essential amino acids)** so our diet must supply these. We produce the remaining 11 by transforming one type into another.

Functions:
1. Structural - Keratin - fingernails, hair
   Collagen - tendons, ligaments
   Proteins- in muscles for contraction
2. Enzymes - speed up chemical reaction (catalyst)
3. Energy Source
4. Hormones - chemical messenger
5. Cell receptors

Structure of an Amino Acid:
   amino group $-NH_2$

   acid group $-COOH^-$
   R group - variable part of the amino acid

Formation of a Peptide:
   peptide bond - bond between a Carbon atom of one amino acid and the Nitrogen atom of another amino acid forming a dipeptide.
   polypeptide - 10 or more amino acids linked together by peptide bonds.

Levels of Structure :
1. **primary structure** - sequence of the different amino acids in a polypeptide chain.
2. **secondary structure** - hydrogen bonds between different amino acids in the chain forming a helix (spiral shape).
3. **tertiary** (tersh-er-airy) **structure** -the final 3 dimensional shape
4. **quaternary structure** - more than one polypeptide chain arranged together. (ex Hemoglobin)

2. Carbohydrates "sugars"- source of energy for our body.

- contain only the elements **C**arbon, **H**ydrogen, **O**xygen (1:2:1 ratio)
   - many H-C-OH groupings " Hydrated Carbons"

Types:
1. **Monosaccharides** - compounds with 3-7 carbons in them
      "simple sugars"
      - often designated (named) according to the number of carbons present.
      - **Pentose sugars** - contain 5 carbons (Ex. Ribose, Deoxyribose)

- **Hexose sugars** - contain 6 carbons (Ex. Glucose, Fructose, Galactose)
> **2. Disaccharides -** two monosaccharides linked together
>> Ex. Glucose + Glucose = Maltose
>>> Glucose + Fructose = Sucrose   "table sugar"
> **3. Polysaccharide -** many monosaccharides linked together.
>> Ex. <u>Glycogen</u> - The form in which humans store excess glucose
>>> <u>Starch</u> - The form in which plants store excess glucose
>>> <u>Cellulose</u> - Structural component of plants. Humans do not possess the enzyme
>>>> needed to break down cellulose so it passes through our digestive tract as
>>>> fiber "roughage".

3. <u>Lipids</u> - Large nonpolar molecules that do not dissolve in water.
- contain carbon, hydrogen, oxygen
> - used as a long term energy source.
- includes fats, oils, cholesterol, steroids, phospholipids
> **<u>Components of a Fats</u>** (triglyceride) most common lipid found in the body.
>> <u>Glycerol</u> molecule - forms the backbone
>> <u>Fatty acids</u> - long carbon chain molecules with attached carbon atoms and an acid group.
>>> <u>saturated fatty acids</u>- no double bonds between the carbons.
>>> <u>unsaturated fatty acids</u> - one or more double bonds between carbon atoms. (Ex. oils)
>>> <u>polyunsaturated fatty acids</u> - many double bonds between carbon atoms.

>> <u>American</u> <u>Heart</u> <u>Association</u> recommends a diet low in saturated fat and cholesterol because of the
>>> its link to Cardiovascular Disease.
> **Cholesterol, Steroids, phospholipids -** to be discussed later.

4. Nucleic Acid -   made up of unit molecules called <u>nucleotides</u>.
> components of a nucleotide:
>> 1. 5 Carbon Sugar Ex. DNA, RNA
>> 2. Nitrogen Base
>> 3. Phosphate Group

5. Vitamins
> **Vitamins** are nutrients required in tiny amounts for essential metabolic reactions in the body.
>> Vitamins are organic molecules that act both as catalysts and substratesin our
>> metabolism.

Circle the correct completion answer within the brackets.

1. The smallest unit of matter is any element is the (atom/molecule).
2. The positive unit in an atom is the (neutron/proton).
3. An electron is (negatively/positively) charged.
4. An electron is (heavier/lighter) than a proton.
5. The addition of more (neutrons/protons) as compared to normal makes an atom radioactive.
6. Sucrose is a (disaccharide/monosaccharide).
7. The number of protons determines the atomic (number/weight).
8. Maltose is made up of glucose and (fructose/glucose).
9. (Helium/Hydrogen) is more likely to explode than (helium/hydrogen).
10. Electrons close to a nucleus have (less/more) energy than those farther away from the nucleus.
11. The sodium and chlorine in salt are held together by (covalent/ionic) bonds.
12. The sodium in salts tends to (give up/take on) an electron.
13. The chlorine in salt is a (negative/positive) ion.
14. In the polar water molecule, the hydrogen region is (negative/positive).
15. Sharing of electrons occurs in (covalent/ionic) bonds.
16. In carbohydrates, the amount of carbon is equal to the amount of (hydrogen/oxygen).
17. In order for two monosaccharides to become a disaccharide, a water molecule must be (added/taken away).
18. Fructose, glucose, and galactose all have (a different/the same) number of carbon, hydrogen, and oxygen atoms.
19. Two glucose molecules join together to form (maltose/sucrose).
20. Animals store their food in the form of (glycogen/starch).
21. (Carbohydrates/Fats) have more energy per gram.
22. Fats are made up of fatty acids and (cholesterol/glycerol).
23. The (hydrophilic/hydrophobic) portion of a phospholipid is located in the center of the cell membrane.
24. Steroids are (straight chain/ring) molecules.
25. The acid portion of an amino acid is the ($^-$COOH/NH$_2$) group.
26. Bonds connecting amino acids are called (disulfide/peptide) bonds.
27. The sequence of amino acids controls the (primary/secondary) structure of proteins.
28. A hemoglobin molecule with only one amino chain would (hold/release) oxygen easier than one with four chains.

ANSWERS TO TEST QUESTIONS

1. atom	16. oxygen	9. hydrogen-helium	24. ring
2. proton	17. taken away	10. less	25. COOH$^-$
3. negative	18. the same	11. ionic	26. peptide
4. lighter	19. maltose	12. give up	27. primary
5. neutrons	20. glycogen	13. negative	28. hold
6. disaccharide	21. fats	14. positive	
7. number	22. glycerol	15. covalent	
8. glucose	23. hydrophobic		

The Cellular Level of Organization

Overview

This chapter presents the fundamentals of structure and function of cells by the analyzing a generalized cell. Important cell processes including diffusion, facilitated diffusion, osmosis, filtration, dialysis, active transport, phagocytosis, and pinocytosis are considered. Attention is also given to the mechanism and importance of cell division and the abnormal divisions of cancer. Gene expression is summarized through DNA transcription by RNA with translation at the ribosomes to explain how proteins are synthesized. The unit concludes with a discussion on cells and aging, the most important disorder of cells--cancer, and a medical terminology list.

Chapter Objectives

1. List the functions of the cell membrane and the structural features that enable it to perform those functions.
2. Specify the routes by which different ions and molecules can enter or leave a cell and the factors that may restrict such movement.
3. Describe the various transport mechanisms that cells use to facilitate the absorption or removal of specific substances.
4. Explain the origin and significance of the trans membrane potential.
5. Describe the organelles of a typical cell, and indicate the specific functions of each.
6. Explain the functions of the cell nucleus.
7. Discuss the nature and importance of the genetic code. 8. Summarize the process of protein synthesis.
9. Describe the stages of the cell life cycle.
10. Describe the process of mitosis, and explain its significance.
11. Define differentiation, and explain its importance.

Concepts and definitions

1. The cell is the structural and functional unit of the human organism.
2. All forms of life contain one or more units known as cells which form the basis of structure and function for that organism.
3. Cells are organized into tissues, tissues into organs, and organs into the systems which are integrated to maintain an individual's life.
4. Each cell possesses a surrounding cell membrane (plasma membrane), that encircles the cytoplasm, and nucleus within the cell to control and direct all cellular activity.

5. The plasma membrane is a protein-lipid complex with receptor proteins that functions as a semipermeable barrier and as a receptor of hormones. (note sketches and photos in your textbook)

6. Modifications of the plasma membrane include microvilli of the small intestine, sacs in rods and cones of the retina, and the myelin sheath of a neuron.

7. Cells take in materials by two methods; *passive and active.*

8. *Passive processes* move materials cross plasma membranes are osmosis, diffusion, facilitated diffusion, filtration, and dialysis.

9. *Active processes* move materials across plasma membranes are active transport, phagocytosis, and pinocytosis.

10. Cytoplasm is the living substance within the confines of the plasma membrane and where metabolic reactions occur.

11. Organelles are specialized structures within the cell that perform such specific functions as: *nucleus*--control center; *endoplasmic reticulum* --transportation and storage network; *ribosomes* --sites for protein synthesis; *golgi complex*--synthesizes, stores, and secretes glycoproteins; *mitochondria* --ATP synthesis; *lysosomes*--contains digestive enzymes; and *cilia or flagella*--movement.

12. Protein synthesis involves the coordinated interaction of DNA, amino acids, several types of RNA, and ribosomes.

13. Cells give rise to other cells by two methods of division; mitosis and meiosis. Differences occur in the manner of division and in the results of the division.

14. The purpose of normal cell division is to replace diseased, damaged, worn-out or non-functional cells back to their original numbers or ratios.

15. Many theories of aging have been proposed, but none successfully answers all the objections or questions.

16. The most important disorder of cells is cancer.

17. A unique property of a malignant tumor is its ability to metastasize. In this process malignant cells invade surrounding and sometimes distant tissues, competing for space and nutrients, sometimes causing the death of the normal tissue.

Summary Outline

The cell is the unit of structure and function of the body. The protoplasm (nucleoplasm + cytoplasm) of all cells has the same chemical composition and possesses similar physical characteristics. Although all cells possess similar physiologic characteristics, cells differentiate and become specialized in a particular function.

I. CONSTITUENTS OF PROTOPLASM
  ### A. Organic Chemical Composition
    1. Proteins contain: Carbon, Hydrogen, Oxygen, Nitrogen, Sulfur, Phosphorus
       Proteins are the most important chemicals of cells; act as enzymes; are essential for metabolism: examples-insulin, hemoglobin, contractile components of muscle, antibodies for immunity
       Colloids: Importance in physiology colloids
         Protoplasm is emulsion of colloids (proteins)
         Holds water within the cell
         Absorb other chemicals at interphase
         Possess electrical charges that contribute to cell metabolism
    2. Carbohydrates contain Carbon, Hydrogen, Oxygen

Carbohydrates are chief source of energy for cells and supply energy needs of body

    3. <u>Lipids</u> contain: Carbon, Hydrogen, Oxygen in extremely low amounts

        Lipids include fats, waxes, phospholipids, and cholesterol; are responsible for structural strength of cell and cell membrane and are involved in maintaining cell membrane permeability

B. <u>Inorganic</u> <u>Chemical</u> <u>Composition</u>:

    Each inorganic substance has an essential role in the maintenance of the functions of the body

      1. <u>Minerals</u>: Sulfur, Phosphorous, Chlorine, Sodium, Potassium, Calcium, Magnesium, Iodine, Iron, Traces of others

      2. <u>Water</u>: Most abundant constituent of cell's intercellular material

        More than two thirds of body weight, More than 75% of non-bone body tissue weight

        Estimate 85-92% of weight of cell

        Physical characteristics having physiologic significance:

        Strong solvent: As to kinds of solutes, As to variable and high concentration of solutes

        Ionizing power is high, Surface tension is high, Specific heat is high,

        Thermal conductivity (for liquids) is high, Latent heat of evaporation is high (a lot of heat is required to evaporate water)

C. <u>Enzymes</u>

    1. Definition: Organic molecules that accelerate the rate of a chemical reaction

    2. Classification:

      Exoenzymes-secreted in an inactive form-activated by another substance function outside of the cell

      Endoenzymes-substances found within cells that promote chemical reactions in the cell

    3. Nature of:

      Are proteins of high molecular weight, Highly specific in action

      Vitamins important in chemical action of enzymes

    4. Characteristics of:

      Act best at body temperature, Require a definite pH to remain functional Action is specific and may be reversible

II. <u>CELL</u> <u>PHYSIOLOGY</u>

    A. Metabolism-life activities of cells

      1. *Anabolism*-building process-formation of larger molecules and their conversion into living substance-"synthesis reactions"

      2. *Catabolism* -forming smaller molecules from larger ones with release of energy "destructive reactions"

    B. Characteristics of living cells

      1. Motion- a. Ameboid movement, b. Ciliary movement

      2. Irritability- ability to respond to stimuli and to conduct the stimuli throughout the cell

      3. Respiration- Provides oxygen for oxidation, Liberates heat, Removes excess carbon dioxide

      4. Circulation- streaming of the protoplasm of the cell

      5. Use of nutrients- foods may also be oxidized to yield energy and regulate body process

      6. Excretion- discharge of waste substances

      7. Cell division- mitosis, meiosis

III. CELL STRUCTURE

The cell is a microscopic unit of protoplasm contained within the cell membrane; protoplasm of the cell is called cytoplasm; cytoplasm contains organelles and inclusion bodies; most cells of the body have a nucleus; protoplasm of nucleus is called karyoplasm.

The human body is composed of 70 trillion cells.
The size and shapes of cells vary according to their function.

Composite cell- a hypothetical cell that possesses all known cell structures.
  Cells have two major parts:
    1. **nucleus** enclosed by a thin membrane called the nuclear envelope .
    2. **cytoplasm**-fluid surrounding the nucleus. Floating within the cytoplasm are specialized structures called *organelles*, each having its own metabolic function. The cytoplasm is surrounded by the plasma membrane.

A. Cell(plasma)Membrane
  -outer boundary of the cell
  -is flexible, is fluid in consistency
  -acts as a *selectively permeable membrane* - lets some substances through while it prevents others
    from entering the cell.
  structure
    -two layers (bilayer) of *phospholipids* with protein molecules floating within it.
  membrane proteins
    1. channel proteins - allow water soluble substances to enter/leave cell.
    2. carrier proteins - transport substances across the plasma membrane
    3. self Identity markers
    4. receptors
    5. enzymes

B. Cytoplasmic organelles -a subunit or substructure within the cell, each with a specific function in the maintenance of the cell

  1. **endoplasmic reticulum** (ER)-network of interconnecting membranes.
     Communicates with the nuclear envelope, plasma membrane and certain organelles
     Two types of ER:
       rough ER(RER)-ER which has its surface covered with numerous *ribosomes*. Ribosomes
         function in the synthesis of proteins, therefore RER is responsible for protein synthesis.
       smooth ER(SER)-lacks ribosomes. Synthesizes important lipids.

  2. **ribosomes**-composed of protein and RNA. Their function is to synthesize proteins.
       Two types, based on location:
       a. free-float freely in the cytoplasm. Synthesize proteins which will be used within the cell.
       b. RER- ribosomes attached to ER. Synthesis of proteins which are packaged and released
         from the cell.

  3. **golgi apparatus** (complex)- stacked membranous sacs, usually found near nucleus. Is
         continuous with ER.
       Function: modifies proteins synthesized in the RER by adding sugar molecules to form

glycoproteins. Once modification is complete, <u>transport</u> <u>vesicles</u> pinch off from the Golgi. These vesicles may:
  a. move to cell membrane and release proteins to exterior of cell
      ex. milk secretion from mammary gland cell
  b. remain within the cytoplasm
      ex. *lysosomes*-vesicles in the cytoplasm which contain digestive enzymes which digest worn out cell parts or ingested substances.

  4. **mitochondria** -powerhouse of the cell.
     Double membrane organelle. Inner layer has numerous infoldings called <u>cristae</u>. Cristae contain enzymes which aid in the production of ATP, a molecule which provides the energy for cellular activities.

  5. **lysosomes**- membranous vesicles which contain powerful catabolic enzymes.
     <u>Function</u>: to digest worn out cell parts; in WBCs they digest ingested bacteria and other foreign particles.

  6. **centrosome**- located near nucleus; consists of two centrioles
     <u>Function</u>: distribution of chromosomes during mitosis and meiosis.

  7. **cilia** - motile processes located on the surface of some cells.
     <u>Function</u>: movement of mucous, fluids along surface of an organ.
         ex. respiratory tract, oviduct.

  8. **flagella**-long usually single projections on the cell surface.
     <u>Function</u>: movement of cell or movement of fluids along the surfaces of cells. (ex. sperm)

  9. **microfilaments**-tiny protein rods usually arranged in network or bundles. <u>Function</u>: cellular movement.
       (ex. *myofilaments* of muscle cells(actin and myosin)

  10. **microtubules**-rigid tubes made of globular proteins. Function: Gives structural support to the cell and also to cilia and flagella. Aids in the transport of substances through cells.
       ex. distribution of chromosomes in mitosis, meiosis. axoplasmic flow in nerve cells.

C. **Nucleus**
   <u>Function</u>: regulates activities of entire cell. Part of the cell which contains DNA which is the "blueprint" for all proteins made by the cells.
   Parts of the nucleus:
       1. <u>nuclear membrane(envelope)</u>- double layered membrane which contains <u>nuclear pores</u> which allows communication between the nucleus and the cytoplasm.
       2.<u>nucleoplasm</u>- fluid contained within the nucleus
       3.<u>nucleolus</u>- structure within the nucleus which produces ribosomes.
       4.<u>chromatin</u>- the DNA of the cell is contained in these strands.

IV. <u>MITOSIS</u>
   A. Cell Division.
   The formation of two new identical cells; during process of mitosis chromosomes of the nucleus divide into two exact sets, and the cytoplasm is constricted to form two new cells; each new daughter cell has the same number of chromosomes and genes
   B. Stages: Interphase, Prophase, Metaphase, Anaphase, Telophase

V. GENETIC CODE

Gene-pairs of nucleotides arranged in specific sequence on a portion of DNA molecule; the biologic unit of heredity, a section of DNA responsible for the synthesis of a specific trait

DNA directs formation of RNA

-three types: 1) ribosomal-RNA 2) transfer-RNA, and 3) messenger-RNA

RNA responsible for protein synthesis

VI. BODY FLUIDS

A. LOCATION

1. Intracellular fluid-all of the fluids within a cell
2. Extracellular fluid
   a- Interstitial fluid-encircles or "bathes" all body (non blood) cells
   b- Blood plasma-"tissue fluid", Fluid within whole blood
   c- Lymph-In lacteals, lymph capillaries, lymph nodes, ducts
   d- Serous fluid- Pericardial fluid, Pleural fluid, Peritoneal fluid
   e- Fluids in closed spaces-Cerebrospinal fluid, Endolymph and perilymph of inner ear, Fluids of eyes, Synovial fluid, and fluids of bursae, tendon sheaths

B. SOURCE-

Diffused from blood plasma, Diffused from cellular chemistry and fluids

Cell membrane is a two-way filtering and diffusion membrane between all cells and tissue fluid, including capillary cells

C. COMPOSITION-

Chemically and physically similar to blood plasma and protoplasm

D. FUNCTION-

Provide necessary cell nutrients and collect metabolic wastes, Regulate and cool temperature of organs and systems

PASSAGE OF MATERIAL ACROSS THE CELL MEMBRANE

Passive Transport Processes-processes in which there is no input of energy. Movement is from areas of high concentration to areas of low concentration (concentration gradient).

1. **Diffusion**-movement of substances from regions where they are in high concentration high to regions of lower concentration. ex. sugar cube in H_2O, open bottle of perfume.

   equilibrium-this process(diffusion) will continue until all the molecules are equal distance apart.

   *substances that diffuse easily through cell membranes are O_2, H_2O, CO_2, fat soluble substances, steroid hormones.

2. **Facilitated diffusion**-process in which carrier molecules transport substances from a region of higher concentration to regions of lower concentration. Rate is limited by the number of carriers.

   ex. **glucose** into glucose resistant muscle cells, kidney tubules and arteries of the eyes.

3. **Osmosis**-similar to diffusion. Movement of water molecules from an area of high water concentration to an area of lower water concentration through a selectively permeable membrane (cell membrane)

   selectively permeable membrane-membrane that allows some substances to move through freely while preventing the passage of other substances.

tonicity-for our purposes we will look at tonicity as a comparison of a solution to the inside (cytoplasm) of the cell.

    solution- solute + solvent

    solute-a substance which is dissolved in a liquid

    solvent-the liquid in which substances are dissolved

        ex. sugar(solute) can be dissolved in H_2O(solvent)

        $NaCl$(solute) can be dissolved in H_2O(solvent)

A. **Isotonic solution**-a solution in which the solute concentration is equal to the inside of the cells. No net (result) movement of water will occur. Cell size stays the same. *Normal Physiological Blood Solute Concentrations*:

    1. NaCl = 0.9% (saline)

    2. glucose = 5.0% (dextrose)

B. **Hypertonic solution**-a solution in which the solute concentration is greater than that of another solution. If a cell is in a hypertonic solution it will undergo crenation (shrink). *"Hypertonic solutions draw or gain water"*

C. **Hypotonic solution**-a solution in which the solute concentration is lower than that of another solution. If a cell is in a hypotonic solution it will swell and possibly burst (**hemolyze**). *"Hypotonic solutions lose water"*

D. **Osmotic pressure** - the amount of pressure needed to stop the net movement of water. In the body the osmotic pressure is due to non-diffusible solutes (proteins, electrolytes, sugars) in the solution. *The greater the number of non-diffusible solute particles, the greater the osmotic pressure of that solution.*

Note: Think of solute particles as little magnets which pull water molecules toward them.

4. **Filtration** –a separation of substances under pressure through a semipermeable membrane. The separation is based on the size.

        ex.kidney filtering the blood

    formation of cerebrospinal fluid

Active Transport Processes-processes which require an input of energy to occur. Is capable of moving substances from areas of low concentration to areas of higher concentration. Requires carrier molecules.(a protein embedded in the membrane) and requires ATP energy.

1. **Active Transport**-involves the movement of materials across the cell membrane against a concentration gradient and requires a source of energy, ATP

  ex. **Na^+,K^+ pump** in neurons, **Ca^{+2} pump** in muscle cells, absorption in digestive tract

2. **Endocytosis**-process in which large particles can enter a cell.

  Two types:

    1. **pinocytosis**-cell take in dissolved particles in the surrounding liquid through vesicles formation.

      ex. cells take in some peptides in this fashion

    2. **phagocytosis**-cells taking in larger particles.

      ex. WBCs engulfing bacteria

3. **Exocytosis** - process in which substances stored in vesicles are secreted from cells

Body Fluid Compartments
1. **Intracellular fluid compartment**-the fluid which is contained within all the cells (i.e. within the cell membrane). Is about 65% of total body water.
2. **Extracellular fluid compartment**-all fluids outside the cells. Is About 35% of total body water.
   a. **interstitial(intercellular) fluid**-fluid which surrounds and bathes the cells.
   b. **plasma**-fluid portion of the blood
   c. **lymph**-fluid within lymphatic vessels

Example of a disturbances in fluid balance between blood, interstitial fluid and cells.

Starvation, kidney failure, or liver disease can result in:
   a. a decrease in the plasma proteins resulting in
   b. a decrease in the osmotic pressure of the blood
   c. water moves out of blood and into the interstitial spaces
   d. swelling (*edema*) results.

CANCER

Mitosis is a unique feature of living cells to permit the passing of genetic information into new cells. It is vital for cells of tissues and organs to regenerate thereby replacing dead or injured cells with exact copies of the parent cells. Also, its important to increase the number of cells produced in response to a stimulus. In this way cells are able to achieve homeostasis in the body. However, when multiplication and replacements becomes excessive or disorganized, cancer results.

What is cancer and what properties do cancer cells have which separate them from other mitotic cells? Neoplasia means new growth and tumor denotes swelling. Obviously not all neoplasms and tumors are cancer. New cells that grow, differentiate (that is, specialize) and express specific characteristics of the parent cells are considered benign.(harmless). However, when the ability to differentiate or specialize is lost, the neoplasm is considered malignant. Malignant cells have the following characteristics separating them from normal cells. **First**, the malignant cells are clonal meaning they originate from the same single defective cell. Thus, there is only one type of cell in a particular cancer. Although there are different types of lung cancer, for example, all the cells are the same for any given type of lung cancer. The **second** property is autonomy. Normal cell proliferation is influenced and controlled by a number of intracellular and extracellular factors. However, malignant cells do not respond to these factors and grow at an increased rate, and have an infinite capacity to replicate, grow in dense concentrations and in a variety of environments. In other words, the mitosis of cancer cannot be regulated or controlled by body mechanisms. Anaplasia is the **third** characteristic of malignancies. Anaplastic cells show abnormal maturation and are often found in immature forms. Although neoplasms can exhibit varying degrees of maturation, the less differentiated the cells, the worse the malignancy. The grade of the tumor reflects the degree of cancer differentiation (or anaplasia). The **fourth** characteristic is the ability to metastasize. Malignant cells can lose their adherence to adjacent cells and thus become able to spread to adjacent or distant tissues within the body. The lymphatic and circulatory systems become the route for metastasizing. It is interesting that particular cancers metastasize to specific locations and this has important implications in treating cancers. The presence of metastasis indicates the worst of prognosis. The stage of a tumor indicates the extent to which it has spread in the body.

SOURCE: Science and Cancer, U.S. Department of Health and Human Services

Neoplasms

Neoplasm - a new and abnormal formation of tissue (tumor).
I. Characteristics of neoplasms:
    A. two broad types:
        1. benign-good tumor. -**B**-(used below)
        2. malignant-bad tumor.(malus means bad)-**M**-(used below)
    B. end in the suffix -oma.
    C. name is based on the cell type of origin:
        1. malignant tumors of epithelial origin are classified as **carcinomas**.
            ex. cancer of basal cells of epidermis=*basal cell carcinoma*.
        2. malignant tumors of muscle or connective tissue origin are classified as **sarcomas**.
            ex. cancer of bone=*osteosarcoma*.
        3. benign tumors of a tissue simply end in -oma.
            ex. tumor of a <u>gland</u>=**adenoma**
                tumor of <u>muscle</u>=**myoma**
                tumor of <u>adipose</u>=**lipoma**

II. Characteristics of benign and malignant neoplasms:
    A. <u>cell characteristics</u>:
        <u>**B**</u>:   well differentiated cells, resemble normal cells.
        <u>**M**</u>:   cells bear little resemblance to normal cells. Altered nuclear size and shape.
            As a general rule, the more abnormal the appearance, the more malignant the cancer

    B. <u>mode of growth</u>
        <u>**B**</u>:   does not invade surrounding tissues, usually encapsulated.
        <u>**M**</u>:   infiltrates and destroys surrounding tissues.

    C. <u>rate of growth</u>:
        <u>**B**</u>:   usually slow.
        <u>**M**</u>:   variable, the more rapid the rate, the more dangerous the cancer.

    D. **metastasis** - the movement of body cells from one part of the body to another. (results in
            secondary growth of a tumor)
        <u>**B**</u>:   none.
        <u>**M**</u>:   can spread to rest of body via lymph and blood.

    E. <u>General effects</u>:
        <u>**B**</u>: remains localized. Not serious unless tumor interferes with important body functions.
        <u>**M**</u>: usually has generalized effects of anemia, weight loss, weakness.

    F. Destruction of tissue:
        <u>**B**</u>:   unlikely.
        <u>**M**</u>:   often causes extensive tissue damage.

    G. Fatal?
        <u>**B**</u>:   rare
        <u>**M**</u>:   will usually cause death unless growth can be controlled.
III. Grading and Staging:
    A. **Grading**-classification of tumors into four categories based on the degree to which cells are
            altered in size, shape, and organization.
        Grade I-closely resemble normal cells.
        Grade IV-altered dramatically from normal cells.

B. **Staging**-based on the progression of tumor growth and development.

TNM system-

T-stands for tumor. T1->T4 denoting increasing tumor size.

N-refers to regional lymph nodes. N1->N3 indicates increasing nodal disease.

M-refers to metastasis. M1-M3 indicates increasing degrees of metastasis.

IV. Causes:

A. environmental-cigarette smoke, pollution, UV radiation, diet, et cetera.

B. viruses

C. genetics or family history--oncogenes-genes that have the ability to transform a normal cell into a cancerou

V. Prevention:

A. reduce fat intake, increase fiber

B. minimize exposure to known carcinogens.

C. good genetics or family tree (obviously beyond or control)

"All diseases are genetically controlled but environmentally influenced" Dr. Ed Krol

---

Practice Test Questions

Matching

1. Cell
2. Plasma (cell) membrane
3. Permeability
4. Semipermeable
5. Pinocytosis
6. Cytoplasm
7. Organelles
8. Adenosine triphosphate (ATP)

9. Meiosis
10. Mitosis
11. Nucleolus
12. Forty-six
13. Phagocytosis
14. Osmosis
15. Sixty

16. Colloids
17. Solute
18. Diffusion
19. Filtration
20. Tissues
21. Organs
22. Systems
23. Enzymes
24. Nucleus

_____ a. Ease with which a substance passes through a membrane.
_____ b. Active process. Membrane "sinks."
_____ c. Formed structures within the cytoplasm
_____ d. Basis of "life" itself
_____ e. Most widely used energy-rich compound in the body.
_____ f. Engulfing of a particle by cytoplasmic flow
_____ g. Determines the passage of material
_____ h. Degree of differential control on passage of materials through a membrane
_____ i. Cell substance within the plasma membrane
_____ j. Composed chiefly of RNA
_____ k. Normal number of chromosomes in the human
_____ l. Formation of new cell identical to old cell
_____ m. Forms haploid cells in gonads
_____ n. Average percent of water in the cell
_____ o. Formed by suspension of proteins and large molecules in the body
_____ p. Passage of solvent water through a membrane
_____ q. Two or more tissues in a larger unit having specific functions
_____ r. Movement of materials primarily by molecular motion
_____ s. Organic catalysts; alter rates of chemical reactions
_____ t. Movement of materials by pressure
_____ u. Several organs working toward some larger goal
_____ v. Cells that are similar in structure and function
_____ w. The part of the cell playing largest role in heredity
_____ x. The dissolved substance

Multiple Choice

1. The "cell theory" as stated by Schleiden and Schwann indicated that:

a. all cells come from pre-existing cells

b. cells metabolize substances

c. cell form the basis of structure in living organisms

d. membranes form the basis of cell structure

2. Factors which determine the permeability of a membrane include: (select all that apply)
   a. amount of water for dilution
   b. concentration differences
   c. pressure gradients
   d. substance size, electrical charge, fat solubility, and carriers

3. The cell's activity is directed by the:
   a. nucleus   b. ribosome
   c. mitochondria   d. lysosome

4. Enzymes are formed by:
   a. carbohydrates   b. proteins
   c. lipids   d. hormones

5. The process of mitosis is utilized as a basis for:
   a. Growth and cell replacement   b. Diversity in chromosome number
   c. Diversity in genetic potential   d. Formation of cells different from the parent

6. Metabolism may be tested for by noting:
   a. oxygen consumption   b. carbon dioxide production
   c. utilization of energy sources   d. all of the above

7. Structurally and functionally, muscle cells have in common:
   a. they form sheets around hollow organs   b. they are irritable and conductile
   c. length and contractility   d. they connect and support

8. Indicators that living processes occur include:
   a. movement, metabolism, breathing   b. movement, irritability, and metabolism
   c. metabolism, ejection, and excretion   d. movement, breathing, and pulse rate

9. Separation of chromosomes occur in which phase of mitosis:
   a. prophase   b. metaphase
   c. anaphase   d. telophase

10. Glucose (a monosaccharide) and glycogen (a polysaccharide) serve as:
    a. energy sources and storage forms   b. insulators to conserve body heat
    c. primary structural materials   d. high energy substances for direct cell use

11. Water is useful in regulation of body temperature because:
    a. it increases the blood volume   b. in increases the urinary output
    c. it has a high heat capacity   d. it has a low heat capacity

12. The sites of protein synthesis in the cell are in the:
    a. Mitochondria   b. ribosomes
    c. Lysosomes   d. Phagosomes

Completion

1. Cells carry on the following activities:

2. The three basic parts of a cell are:

3. The activities of a cell are similar to the activities of a whole organism.

Cell Part	Function
Plasma membrane	_____
Cytoplasm	_____
ER	_____
Ribosomes	_____
Mitochondria	_____
Golgi apparatus	_____
Central body	_____
Lysosome	_____
Vacuoles	_____
Fibrils	_____
Tubules	_____
Inclusions	_____
Nucleus	_____

4. The five stages in mitosis are:

5. Chromosomes duplicate themselves during the _____ stage in mitosis.

6. Enzymes may be classified by:

7. The suffix - ___added to the name of the substance upon which it acts, is used to form the name of an enzyme.

8. Give the general name and specific example of an enzyme for each of the following substrates.

Substrate	Name	Example
Carbohydrates		
Proteins		
Fats		

9. Four ways in which passive and active processes differ are:

      Active   *Passive*

  a.

  b.

  c.

  d.

10. The four body tissue groups are:

  1.   2.

  3.   4.

11. Three functions of inorganic salts are:

  1.   2.

  3.

12. Osmosis depends on _____ of solute.

STUDY QUESTIONS- with answers

1] During glycolysis
 a. glucose is reduced
 b. FAD is reduced
 c. NAD+ is oxidized
 d. PGAL is oxidized (**)

2] What does the following equation represent?
  Glucose ------> lactic acid + 2 ATP

 a. anaerobic respiration (**)
 b. aerobic respiration
 c. hydrolysis
 d. phosphorylation

3] Each 6-carbon glucose molecule produces
 a. one pyruvic acid + CO_2
 b. 2 acetyl CoA (**)
 c. 3, 2-C intermediates
 d. 4 PGAL

4] How many CO_2 molecules are released in two cycles of the Krebs Cycle?
  a.1 b.2 c.3 d.4 (**)

5] The final H (hydrogen atom) acceptor in aerobic respiration is

 a. NAD^+ b. pyruvic acid   c. carbon
 d. oxygen (**)

6. Anaerobic respiration is less efficient than aerobic respiration because
    a. alcohol has unused stored energy (**)
    b. anaerobic respiration needs more activation energy
    c. CO_2 is not released from the glucose
    d. excessive oxygen is available

7. Which one of the following will provide the energy for active transport?
    a. loss of a phosphate from ATP (**)
    b. loss of a phosphate from ADP
    c. addition of a phosphate to ATP
    d. addition of a phosphate to ADP

8. The release of energy from a molecule by the removal of a hydrogen atom is
    a. dehydration synthesis   b. reduction
    c. hydrolysis   d. oxidation(**)

TRUE OR FALSE
9. ADP contains 2 phosphates. (T)
10. Carrier molecules transport H atoms. (T)
11. ATP is a nucleotide. (T)
12. The energy released from the oxidation of food is stored in the bonds of ATP. (T)
14. NAD^+ and FAD are carrier molecules. (T)
15. ATP has three phosphates. (T)
16. Converting ATP into ADP releases energy. (T)
17. ATP contains more chemical energy than ADP. (T)

ANSWERS

Matching
1. d   2. g   3. a   4. h   5. b   6. i   7. c   8. e   9. m   10. 1
11. j   12. k   13. f   14. p   15. n   16. o   17. x   18. r   19. t   20. v
21. q   22. u   23. s   24. w

Multiple Choice
1. c   2. d   3. a   4. b   5. a   6. d   7. c   8. b   9. c   10. a   11. c   12. b

Completion
1. Respond to stimuli; ingest materials; metabolize materials for energy; synthesize new materials; rid themselves of waste; reproduce their kind.
2. membrane, cytoplasm, and nucleus.
3. note: refer to your lecture textbook
4. Interphase, Prophase, Metaphase, Anaphase, Telophase.
5. Prophase
6. Substrate, type of activity, where act.
7. -ase
8.

Name	Example
Carbohydrates	Lactase
Proteases	Pepsin
Hydrolases	Lipase

9.

Active	Passive
a. Cell participates	Cell does not participate
b. Moves at constant rate	Slows as equilibrium is approached
c. Does not depend on gradients	Depends on gradients
d. Does not attain equilibrium	Tends to attain equilibrium

10. Epithelial, connective, muscular, nervous
11. Create osmotic gradients aid in buffering; aid in creating irritability.

12. Numbers of solute particles and not the different types.

The Tissue Level of Organization

(Histology)

Overview

The primary concern of this unit is the organization of cells into tissues. The structure, function, and location of the principal types of epithelium and connective tissues are examined. Throughout the chapter, the relationships between structure and function are emphasized. Also, attention is given to mucous, serous, and synovial membranes. The unit concludes with a discussion of tissue inflammation and repair both of which are homeostatic mechanisms.

Chapter Objectives

1. Identify the four major tissue types of the body and their roles.
2. Discuss the types and functions of epithelial cells.
3. Describe the relationship between form and function for each epithelial type.
4. Compare the structures and functions of the various types of connective tissues.
5. Explain how epithelial and connective tissues combine to form four types of membranes, and specify the functions of each.
6. Describe how connective tissue establishes the framework of the body.
7. Describe the three types of muscle tissue and the special structural features of each type.
8. Discuss the basic structure and role of neural tissue.
9. Describe how injuries and aging affect the tissues of the body.

Concepts and definitions

1. A tissue is an aggregation of cells working together to perform a specialized function.
2. Epithelial tissue covers or lines body structures and is part of all glands.
3. Each type of epithelium consists of specifically shaped cells and specifically layered patterns for specific functions.
4. Glandular epithelium is organized into exocrine or endocrine glands.
5. Connective tissue differs from epithelium with regard to location, vascular supply, density of cells, and composition of matrix.
6. The cells and interstitial matrix of connective tissue are unique and identify their functions
7. A membrane is a layer of epithelium, together with an underlying layer of connective tissue that nourishes the epithelium.
8. The principal membranes of the body are *mucous, serous, synovial,* and *cutaneous.*
9. Damaged tissues cause an inflammatory response that includes *redness, pain, heat, swelling,* and sometimes a *loss of function.*
10. The stages of the inflammatory response include: **1)** vasodilation and increased permeability of blood vessels, **2)** phagocyte migration, **3)** release of nutrients, **4)** fibrin formation, and **5)** pus formation.

11. Repair of an injured tissue toward normal function depends on whether *parenchymal* or *stroma* cells are active in the repair process.
12. Among the conditions that affect repair are nutrition, degree of circulation, and age.

Summary Outline

Cells having similar structural characteristics and functions are grouped together to form a tissue.

Primary Tissues
Epithelial
Connective
Muscle
Nervous

I. **EPITHELIAL TISSUE**
A. GENERAL CHARACTERISTICS
1. Lines and covers body surfaces
2. Forms glandular tissue
3. No direct blood supply, that is, avascular
4. Little surrounding extracellular space; cells closely packed together
5. Epithelial cells held together by projections on lateral cell surface
6. Apical surface of columnar epithelial cells modified to form microvilli, characteristic of digestive system, and cilia, characteristic of respiratory tract
7. Basal layer of epithelial cells rest on a *basement membrane*
8. Three shapes of cells-squamous, columnar, and cuboidal
9. Arrangement-one layer (simple), many layers (stratified)

B. FUNCTIONS
1. Protection
2. Secretion
3. Absorption
4. Special sensation; specialized neuroepithelium; examples-eye, ear, nose

C. EPITHELIUM - Most Common Types (arrangement and functions)
Simple squamous-as *endothelium* it lines the heart, blood, and lymph vessels and forming capillary networks-as *mesothelium* it lines serous cavities and covers visceral organs; ease of exchange of materials due to one-cell-layer thickness
Simple cuboidal-found in many glands, lines kidney tubules, tissue adapted for secretion and absorption
Simple columnar-as lining of digestive tract, stomach, small and large intestine; in small intestine epithelial cells with microvilli predominate; function of microvilli is to increase surface area for absorption
Pseudostratified-one layer of cells but appear as many layers; pseudostratified with goblet cells lines most of the respiratory passages
Stratified squamous-many cell layers, adapted for protection; forms epidermis of skin
Transitional-many cell layers, lines hollow organs that are subject to shape changes due to contraction and distention, such as the urinary bladder

II. **CONNECTIVE TISSUE**
General Characteristics
1. Provides the structure that supports epithelium and other tissues; essential role in transport, protection, and tissue repair
2. Greater proportion of extracellular material in relation to the volume of cells present

A. CONNECTIVE TISSUE PROPER
Loose (areolar) connective tissue-Composition: many collagenous fibers, some elastic and some reticular fibers; cells of the tissue are fibroblasts, macrophages, plasma cells, mast cells, adipose cells, and blood cells
Function: connects, insulates, forms protecting sheaths, and is continuous throughout the whole body; interstitial fluid matrix is called tissue fluid, often called internal environment of a structure, serves as a medium for transfer of solutes from blood and lymph vessels to cells, and wastes from cells to blood and lymph; stores water, salts, and glucose
Dense irregular connective tissue-collagenous bundles thicker, more numerous, and randomly woven into compact framework; typically seen in dermis of skin
Connective tissue proper *(continued)*
Dense regular connective tissue (collagenous c.t.)-collagen fibers predominant, arranged in specific pattern; this tissue makes up tendons, ligaments

Elastic connective tissue-elastic fibers predominate; tissue is stretchable and elastic; found in walls of arteries, trachea, bronchial tubes, and vocal folds of voice box

Reticular tissue-predominant fiber type is reticular, this tissue makes up stroma of liver, spleen, and lymphoid organs, assists in the immune response

Adipose tissue-cells filled with lipids; found throughout body wherever loose connective tissue found; important reserve of food, which may be utilized for energy; supports and protects various organs

B. CARTILAGE.

Cartilage consists of a group of cells in a gel-like interstitial matrix. It is firm, tough, and elastic, covered, avascular and nourished by perichondrium

1. Hyaline cartilage

Costal - connects ribs to sternum

Articular - ends of moving bones

2. Fibrocartilage (location-intervertebral disk, symphysis pubis)
3. Elastic cartilage (location: external ear, epiglottis)

C. BONE

1. Types

a. Compact (hard) (vascular)

b. Cancellous (spongy) (relatively avascular)

2. Vascularization

a. Compact bone - contains Haversion canals protecting arteries, veins and nerves

b. Spongy bone - remnants of compact bone that lightens weight and increases strength

3. Connective tissue within medullary cavity and spongy bone

a. Red marrow (myeloid tissue), very vascular hematopoietic

b. Yellow marrow (myeloid tissue) adipose tissue storage and non-hematopoietic

III. **MEMBRANES**

A. DEFINITION

Any thin expansion of tissues that serves as a lining or covering

B. TYPES

a. Serous membranes

b. Synovial membranes (lack epithelium)

c. Mucous membranes

d. Cutaneous membrane

Consists of

1. Simple squamous epithelium

2. A thin layer of connective tissue that nourishes the epithelium.

Derived from the mesoderm and called mesothelium

C. LOCATION

1. Located as a liner of closed cavities or passages that do not communicate with the exterior.

2. Lining the body cavities and covering the organs that lie in them

Three classes

a. Pleura - cover the lungs and line the inner surface of the chest

b. Pericardium-covers the heart and lines the outer fibrous pericardium

c. Peritoneum-covers the abdominal and the top of some of the pelvic organs, lines the abdominal cavity

3. Inner lining of the vascular system

Heart, arteries, veins and lymphatic vessels

D. FUNCTIONS

1. Protection - physical and chemical

2. Furnishes a cover or lining for viscera

3. Serous membranes reduce friction between contacting structures

Figure 2 Organization of epithelial tissue

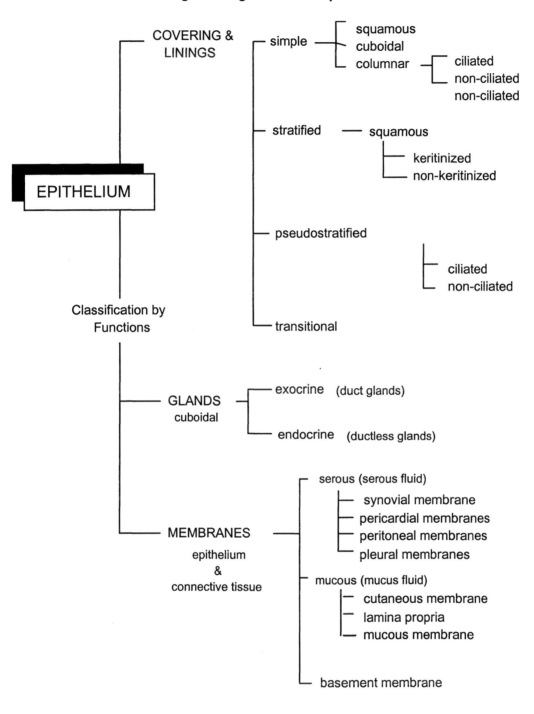

Figure 3 Organization of major connective tissues flow chart

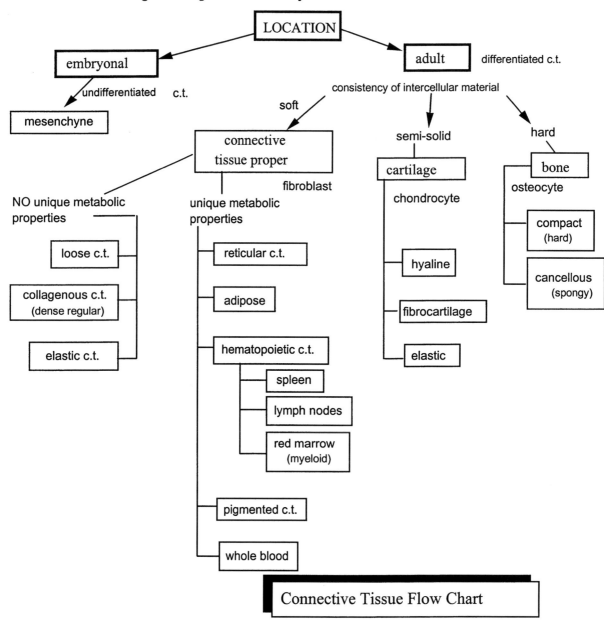

Connective Tissue Flow Chart

The Integumentary System

The Skin

Overview

This unit introduces the organ and system levels of organization by considering the structure and functions of the skin and its epidermal derivatives such as hair, glands, and nails. A major concept developed is the role of the skin in the homeostasis of body temperature as part of a negative feedback system. Disorders of the skin discussed are acne, impetigo, systemic lupus erythematosis, psoriasis, decubitus, sunburn, skin cancer, and burns. There is a glossary of medical terminology at the end of the chapter. The chapter concludes with an explanation of the actions of selected drugs associated with the integumentary system.

Chapter Objectives

1. Describe the main structural features of the epidermis, and explain their functional significance.
2. Explain what accounts for individual and racial differences in skin, such as skin color.
3. Discuss the effects of ultraviolet radiation on the skin and the role played by melanocytes.
4. Describe the functions of the integumentary system
5. List the structures of the dermis, epidermis and subdermis.
6. Describe the cellular structures of the integumentary system.
7. Discuss and describe the structure, function and interaction of the component parts of the integumentary system.
8. Discuss the role of the skin and its circulation in heat conservation and dissipation.
9. Describe the skin in homeostasis.
10. Describe changes in the skin throughout a person's lifespan.
11. Describe the structure and functions of the dermis.
12. Describe the structure and functions of the subcutaneous layer.
13. Explain the mechanisms that produce hair, and determine hair texture and color.
14. Discuss the various kinds of glands in the skin and the secretions of those glands.
15. Explain how the sweat glands of the integumentary system play a major role in regulating body temperature.
16. Describe the anatomical structure of nails and how they are formed.
17. Explain how the skin responds to injury and repairs itself.
18. Summarize the effects of the aging process on the skin.
19. Give examples of interactions between the integumentary system and each of the other organ systems.

Concepts and Definitions

1. An organ consists of several tissues and performs specialized activities. The tissues comprising the skin are the epithelium of the epidermis and the connective tissues of the dermis.
2. Epithelial tissues cover, line, protect, absorb, secrete, and may contain sensory receptors. Their cells fit closely together, are avascular (nonvascular), and have great regenerative capacity.
3. A system is a group of organs that performs specialized activities. The organs of the integumentary system are the skin, hair, nails, glands, and sensory receptors.
4. Among the functions of the skin are protection, control of body temperature, the reception of stimuli, excretion, and synthesis of several compounds.
5. There are two varieties of skin (thick and thin), each containing three major layers.
6. Skin is "the first line of defense" in protecting the body against bacterial and viral infections.
7. Skin is 1) elastic, 2) prevents passage of charged substances in either direction, 3) is provided with antiseptic and water proofing substances, 4) absorbs gases and lipid soluble substances, 5) regulates body temperature, and 6) synthesizes several important chemicals.
8. Epithelial membranes (serous and mucous) consist of a cellular layer and an underlying connective tissue layer.
9. Skin color depends on pigments and blood flow.
10. Connective tissues 1) connect and support, 2) are not usually found on surfaces, 3) are generally vascular, 4) have intercellular material that is usually fibrous. There are many varieties within the skin.
11. The skin develops from 2 sources, ectoderm (epidermis) and mesoderm (dermis and hypodermis or subcutaneous).
12. Accessory organs of the skin include hair, nails, and glands.
13. Glands are typically of epithelial origin.
14. The skin helps to maintain the homeostasis of body temperature through a negative feedback system.
15. A common disorder of the skin is acne, which is an inflammation of sebaceous glands.
16. Other skin disorders include impetigo, systemic lupus erythematosis, psoriasis, decubitus ulcer, sunburn, an skin cancer.
17. Pigment absence may be total (universal albinism), may be absent in all areas but the iris (generalized albinism), or may be absent only in particular body areas (piebald albinism, white forelock, ocular albinism).
18. Sunburn is an injury to the skin as a result of acute, prolonged exposure to the ultraviolet rays of sunlight. Skin damage is caused by the inhibition of DNA and RNA synthesis.
19. The screening effectiveness of a topical sunscreen is given a numerical rating called the sun protection factor (SPF).
20. Skin reflects the presence of internal and external changes, and may suffer burns.
21. Burns can destroy the proteins in the exposed cells and cause cell injury or death.
22. Burns are classified by depth: first-degree and second-degree burns together are called partial-thickness burns; third-degree burns are termed full thickness burns.
23. The "rule of nines" is used to approximate the extent of burns.
24. Skin absorbs fat soluble vitamins (A,D,E,K) because of its lipid content within the dermis.
25. The pH of the epidermis is approximately 5.5 and dermis is 7.35 and both function as a bacteriostatic chemical protector for the body.
26. An intact (unbroken) skin is the "first line of defense" against infections entering the body.

Summary Outline

The Integumentary system is composed of the organ skin and other various accessory structures (fingernails, toenails, hair, glands).

I. FUNCTIONS
    1. Covers the body
    2. Protects the deeper tissues from drying, injury, invasion by infectious organisms
    3. Important factor in heat regulation
    4. Contains the end organs of many sensory nerves
    5. It has limited excretory and absorbing power
    6. Prevents loss of body fluids
    7. Contains structures for the reception of stimuli

II. STRUCTURES
A. Epidermis
    The tissue is a stratified squamous epithelium, pH 5.5 (acid or base?)
    Layers of the epidermis
    1. Stratum corneum
    2. Stratum lucidum
    3. Stratum granulosum
    4. Stratum spinosum
    5. Stratum basale - only living layer of the epidermis-others are dying or dead layers
      a. the deepest single layer of cuboidal cells that undergo mitosis and thus gives rise to the other layers.
      b. is nourished by the underlying blood vessels in the dermis.
      c. contains pigment producing cells called **melanocytes** - produce the dark pigment melanin which is responsible for skin pigmentation.
      Note: Regardless of ethnic origin, all people have about the same number of melanocytes. Differences in skin color depends on amounts of melanin produced which is genetically controlled.
    As newly formed cells arise from the dividing basal cells layer, they enlarge, push the older epidermal cells (Keritinocytes) away from the dermis towards the surface away from their nutrient supply. Along the way these keritinocytes produce and store the waterproofing protein, Keratin .
    Skin cancers: basal cell carcinoma, squamous cell carcinoma, malignant melanoma

B. Dermis - a layer of connective tissue - pH is equal to blood plasma at 7.4
    1. Papillary layer-papillae are minute conical elevations of the corium. Ridges form the fingerprints They contain looped capillaries, and some contain termination of nerve fibers called tactile corpuscle
    2. Reticular layer - Bands of fibrous and elastic tissue that interlace, leaving tiny spaces that are occupied by adipose tissue and sweat glands

C. Blood vessels - The arteries form a network in the subcutaneous tissue and send branches to papillae and glands of skin. Capable of holding a large proportion of total amount of blood in body

D. Lymphatics There is a superficial and a deep network of lymphatics in the skin

E. Nerve fibers
    1. Motor fibers to blood vessels and arrector muscles

2. Fibers concerned with temperature sense
3. Fibers concerned with sense of touch and pressure
4. Fibers stimulated by pain
5. Fibers that are distributed to the glands

III. APPENDAGES OF THE SKIN
A. Nails
1. Consist of clear, horny cells of epidermis
2. Corium forms a bed, or matrix, for nail
3. Root of nail is lodged in a deep fold of the skin
4. Nails grow in length from soft cells in stratum germinativum at root

B. Hair
1. The hairs grow from the roots
2. The roots are bulbs of soft, growing cells contained in the hair follicles
3. Hair follicles are little pits developed in the corium
4. Stems of hair extend beyond the surface of the skin, consist of three layers of cells:
   (1)cuticle, (2)cortex, and (3)medulla
5. cells move upward from papilla, become keratinized, and then die.
6. once pushed up above the surface of the skin, these now dead cells make up the shaft of the hair.
7. Hair color is genetically determined by the amount of melanin produced by epidermal melanocytes.
   dark hair = much melanin
   blond hair = little melanin
   white hair = no melanin
   red hair   = iron pigment in hair
   gray hair = mixture of pigmented & nonpigmented hair
8. Arrector pili muscles - bundles of smooth muscle cells attached to hair follicles.
   contract and cause hair to stand up (goose bumps) when a person is emotionally upset or very cold.
9. Absent from: a. palms of the hands, soles of the feet, nipples, parts of external reproductive organs, last
   phalanges of the fingers and toes
10. Compound alveolar glands, the ducts of which usually open into a hair follicle but may discharge
    separately on the surface of the skin

C. Sebaceous glands
1. Lie between arrector muscles and hairs
2. Found over entire skin surface except
   a. Palms of hands
   b. Soles of feet
3. Secrete sebum, a fatty, oily substance, which keeps the hair from becoming too dry and brittle, the
   skin flexible, forms a protective layer on surface of skin, and prevents undue absorption or
   evaporation of water from the skin
4. groups of specialized epithelial cells associated with hair follicles.
5. sebum helps keep hair and skin soft and pliable.
6. found throughout the body except on the palms of your hands or soles of your feet.
7. overactive and inflamed sebaceous glands cause acne.

D. Sweat glands -"oil glands"
1. Tubular glands, consist of single tubes with the blind ends coiled in balls, lodged in subcutaneous
tissue, and surrounded by a capillary plexus; secrete sweat and discharge it by means of ducts that
open exteriorly

2. Volume of sweat is *increased* by
    a. Increased temperature or humidity of the atmosphere
    b. Dilute condition of blood
    c. Exercise
    d. Pain
    e. Nausea
    f. Mental excitement or nervousness
    g. Dyspnea
    h. Use of diaphoretics, e.g., pilocarpine, physostigmine, nicotine
    i. Various diseases, such as tuberculosis, acute rheumatism, and malaria
3. Volume of sweat is *decreased* by
    1. Cold
    2. Voiding a large quantity of urine
    3 Diarrhea
    4. Certain drugs, e.g., atropine and morphine
    5. Certain diseases, e.g. Renauds disease, certain types of "Lupus"
4. Activity of sweat glands is due to
    1. Direct stimulation of nerve ending in sweat glands
    2. Indirect stimulation through sensory nerves of the skin
    3. Influenced by external heat, dyspnea, muscular exercise, strong emotions, and the action of various drugs
5. Function of sweat
    1 - Importance not in elimination of waste substances in perspiration, but elimination of heat needed to cause evaporation of perspiration
    2 - When kidneys are not functioning properly, sweat glands will excrete waste substances, especially if stimulated
6. Modified sweat glands
    1. Ceruminous Glands
    2. Found in skin of external auditory canal
    3. Secrete cerumen "<u>ear-wax</u>", a yellow, pasty substance, like wax

Subcutaneous Layer "Hypodermis" - found beneath dermis
  a. consists of a loose fibrous connective tissue and adipose.
  b. the collagen and elastic fibers are continuous with those of the dermis.
  c. adipose thickness varies form one body region to another.
  d. eyelids lack adipose in most races.
  e. contains the major blood vessels supplying skin.

<u>**Membranes**</u> - a thin sheet like structure composed of an epithelium and connective tissue. Found covering surfaces and lining body cavities and organs.

1. <u>Serous membranes</u> - lines body cavities that lack openings to the outside produces a watery serous fluid which lubricates the surfaces of membranes.
    Examples: peritoneum, pleura, pericardium

2. <u>Mucous membranes</u> - lines cavities and tubes that open to the outside of the body. Contains cells that produce mucous
    Examples: oral cavity, nasal cavity, small intestine, trachea

3. Synovial membranes - forms the inner linings of joint cavities between bones

4. Cutaneous membranes - an organ of the integumentary system - Skin.

Lecture Supplements
INFLAMMATION
). Any injury can be thought of as stress and thus inflammation can occur in response to most any stressor.

SYMPTOMS
Inflammation is usually characterized by four basic signs: **redness, pain, heat** and **swelling**. A fifth is a symptom and that is the **loss of function** depending on the extent of the response. The inflammatory response serves a protective and defensive role. It is an attempt to neutralize and destroy any toxic agents at the site of injury and to prevent their spread to other organs. Therefore, the inflammatory response is an attempt to restore homeostasis to the injured site and start the process of healing.

The immediate response to tissue injury consists of a sequence of physiological events. At first, various body components are involved: blood vessels, intercellular fluid called *exudate*, mixes with injured body cells, blood components and surrounding epithelial and connective tissues. Other factors affecting the response to injury are age, extent of injury and general state of overall health. *Healing starts as the inflammatory response comes to an end.*

STAGES
The inflammatory response is one of the major methods used by the body for internal defense. The response that follows is basically the same if the agent was a burn, rusty nail, sore throat, infection or other problems.
The stages are:
1. Vasodilation and increased permeability of blood vessels
   2. Phagocyte migration
   3. Release of nutrients
   4. Fibrin formation
   5. Pus formation

1. Vasodilation and Increased Permeability of Blood Vessels
Immediately following tissue damage vasodilation (increased blood vessel diameter) and increased blood capillary permeability occurs. This increased blood penetrations forms more interstitial fluid and allows more defensive chemicals to invade the area. Such chemicals include white blood cells and clot forming chemicals. The increased blood flow also removes toxic products and dead cells preventing them from complicating the injury. The toxic substances include cellular wastes from the invading microorganisms and chemicals from the person's damaged tissues. If bleeding occurred into the interstitial space and fluids then clotting will occur to trap and prevent the spreading of the microorganisms and toxic chemicals to other parts of the body.

The vasodilation and increased permeability occurred because *histamines* were released from the damaged body tissues. Normally histamine is in the mast cells, basophils (a WBC) and blood platelets. Because of the released histamine, neutrophils are attracted out from the blood and to the injury site. These histamines cause the redness, pain, heat and swelling associated with inflammation. *Kinins* also cause vasodilation, increase blood vessel permeability and along with histamines increase pain.

These kinins also cause neutrophils to invade the area (stage 2) and begin their activity. *Prostaglandins* (PG) are also released and are extremely potent vasodilators and inflammatory agents. Aspirin an antiprostaglandin is an effective mild anti-inflammatory agent that blocks the effect of PGs thus reducing swelling (inflammation).

The metabolism in the area also increases. Within minutes the four main symptoms occur in an attempt to destroy and dilute the cause of the inflammation. Pain in the area can result from injury to nerve fibers.

2. Phagocyte Migration

Generally, within one hour phagocytes (macrophages and microphages) invade the injury site. Blood flow through the blood vessels (capillaries) slows as fluid is lost and blood viscosity (thickness) rises. Certain leukocytes (neutrophils) move to the inner surface of the capillaries (margination), then, by ameboid movement move through the capillary wall (diapedesis) and into the injury site.

Chemotaxic (chemicals that direct) chemicals control the direction of leukocyte travel. The neutrophils attempt to destroy the invading microorganisms by phagocytosis. chemotaxis

As the inflammatory response continues, monocytes follow the neutrophils into the infected area. Once in the area, monocytes become transformed into wandering macrophages that assist the phagocytotic activity of the fixed macrophages normally present in the tissue.

3. Release of Nutrients

Stored nutrients in the area are released to support the defensive cells and their increased metabolism. These many nutrients will also become necessary for the growth and repair of new tissue in the area.

4. Fibrin Formation

The blood releases a soluble protein, fibrinogen, that is converted to an insoluble protein network of fibrin. This net traps and localizes the invading microorganisms or chemicals thus preventing their spread. This network eventually becomes a fibrin clot that prevents hemorrhage and isolates the infected area.

5. Pus Formation

In all but the very mild inflammations pyogenesis occurs. Pus is a thick fluid that contains living and nonliving, white blood cells, normal body tissue and the infectious organisms. Normally, the circulatory system will slowly absorb this pus and clear up the affected area. If it cannot drain into the circulatory system the an abscess develops, that is, pus in a confined space.

A*nother way of summarizing the inflammatory response is by using the two previous flow diagrams but renaming the stages as: 1) Vascular response, 2) Cellular responses, 3) Exudate and 4) Healing. These stages are an alternative method of explanation and are the following paragraphs.*

1-*Vascular Response*

After the tissue injury the capillaries will vasoconstrict for a short time. Next, following the release of histamines, kinins, etc. from the injured cells and normal mast cells the vessels dilate. This vasodilation causes hyperemia (increased blood supply through a tissue) and increased production of interstitial :fluids. Vasodilation along with chemicals makes the capillaries more permeable. Movement of fluids from the capillaries into tissue spaces is facilitated. Initially composed of serous fluid, this inflammatory exudate is later joined by plasma proteins, primarily albumin. These proteins make the interstitial more hypertonic to blood thus causing more fluids to leave the blood capillaries. The tissue then swells or becomes *edematous*.

As the plasma protein, fibrinogen, leaves blood it is changed to fibrin to strengthen the clot formed by the platelets. The clot functions to trap bacteria, preventing their spread and will serve as the structure framework in the healing process that will follow.

The following two flow diagrams summarize this inflammatory response. These flow charts will divide inflammation into 1-the vascular response and 2-cellular response phases.

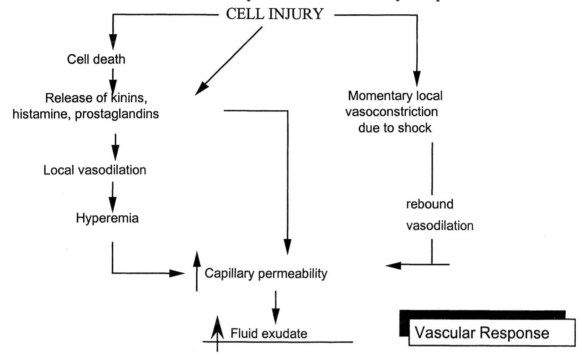

Figure 4 Vascular response in inflammation, flow chart

2- Cellular Response

The blood flow through the capillaries of the area slows as fluid is lost and viscosity rises. Certain leukocytes (WBCs) move to the inner surface of the capillaries (margination), then, by ameboid movement through the capillary wall (diapedesis) and to the injury site.

Chemicals released by injured cells will attract the leukocytes, a process called chemotaxis, out of the circulatory system. The cells respond to the chemicals by moving into the injury site.

NEUTROPHILS Neutrophils are the first leukocytes to arrive. They phagocytize bacteria, other foreign material and damaged body cells. With their short life span dead neutrophils soon accumulate. In time the mixture of dead neutrophils, digested bacteria, and other cell debris causes a creamy white substance called pus.

In order to keep up with the demand for neutrophils, the bone marrow releases more into circulation. This causes an elevated white blood cell count especially for neutrophils.

MONOCYTES Monocytes are the second type of phagocytic cells to migrate from circulating blood to the injury site. Upon entering the tissue spaces, the monocytes transform into macrophages (wandering macrophages). These macrophages with tissue macrophages (fixed macrophages) assist in the phagocytosis of the inflammatory debris. Macrophages have a long life span and are critical to removing

47

debris before healing can begin to occur.

Some macrophages can bind together to wall off the infection or inflammation. This doesn't kill the infection but does check it from spreading. If walled off a chronic state of inflammation can result without the infection getting worse and also without healing occurring. This may or may not become a problem.

LYMPHOCYTES Lymphocytes arrive later and are important in the production of antibodies for future immunity. Immunity will be covered in my BIO 234 lectures.

EOSINOPHILS and BASOPHILS
Eosinophils are released in large amounts in an allergic inflammatory reaction and are thus involved in the immune response that may occur. Basophils release heparin (an anticoagulant) and histamine. The heparin reduces excessive coagulation and thus dangerous coagulation while histamine is the potent vasodilator to maintain blood flow through the tissue.

Figure 5 Cellular response in inflammation, flow chart

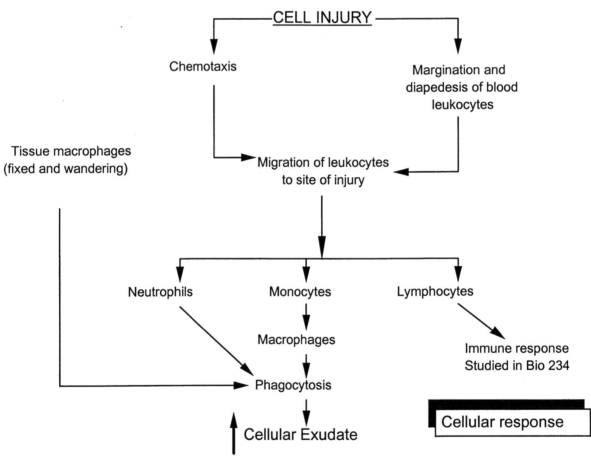

3- Exudate
The exudate (extra fluid and cells) is formed by both fluid and the cells that moved into the site as well as from the tissue's cellular debris. Five different types of exudate are identified but not stated here.

4- Healing
Normally, inflammation is followed by healing. However, if the cause of the inflammation is not removed then healing cannot occur. As a result the inflammation is chronic and persists for a long time.

1. ANTIHISTAMINES

These are effective primarily in the respiratory concha and block the activity of histamine. The damaged tissue releases histamine but is blocked from causing the process of inflammation.

2. CORTICOSTEROIDS "STEROIDS"

These type of steroids are properly called corticosteroids. They reduce and block inflammation by regulating the electrolyte balance in the injured area thus eliminating excessive fluid build up. Also, these drugs return the vessel diameter to their previous diameter and stop the release of extra fluid from the capillaries. Some of the common products are Cortaid (over the counter medication), Decadron, cortisol, etc. In a dilute form it is allowed to be sold over the counter (without a prescription) but when more concentrated is sold only with a written prescription.

3. NON-STEROID (or NSAIDs)

These are potent antiprostaglandin drugs. Injured tissue PGs' are just as potent as histamines and thus when blocked will stop the inflammatory response. Examples of these anti-prostaglandin drugs are Motrin and any of the ibuprofen type medications. In a dilute form it is allowed to be sold over the counter (without a prescription) but when more concentrated it is sold only with a written prescription.

4. ASPIRIN

This is another example of an antiprostaglandin drug but is less potent than any of those in the non-steroid group above. Injured tissue PGs' are just as potent as histamines and thus when blocked will stop the inflammatory response. Tylenol does not reduce inflammation and thus should not be confused with aspirin when trying to reduce pain that is caused by swelling, that is, inflammation.

Figure 6 Antiinflammatory medications, table

Category	Action	Examples
antihistamines	Blocks action of histamines in tissue, therefore no swelling	Benedryl, Dramamine
cortico "steroids"	Blocks inflammation by regulating electrolyte balance. This reduces excessive tissue fluid accumulations	Cortaid, Decadron, cortisol, cortisone
non-steroid (anti-PG's)	Blocks most PG's and aracidonic acid pathways	Ibuprofen, Naprosyn
aspirin (anti PG's)	Blocks some PG's	Bayer, Anacin, Bufferin(the aspirin component)

The Healing process

The final phase of the inflammatory response is healing. Healing includes the two major components of *regeneration* and *replacement*. In regeneration and replacement the body's cells are classified as either parenchyma or stroma cells. Healing's goal is the replacement of lost functional cells and tissues with cells identical to the original ("parenchyma cells") cells. The healing stages also involve the excessive growth of connective tissue that provided structure to the original tissue ("stroma cells"). For example, the cardiac muscle part of the heart is the parenchymal tissue of the heart. The restoration of an injured organ or tissue to normal structure and function depends entirely on which type of cell - parenchyma or stroma - is active and dominates during the repair process. If only parenchymal elements accomplish the repair, a perfect or near perfect reconstruction of the injured tissue occurs.

However, if fibroblasts of the stroma are active in the repair, the tissues will be replaced with mainly new connective tissue called scar tissue (stroma). In this case, fibroblasts synthesize excessive collagen and other proteins that accumulate to form scar tissue. This process of scar tissue formation is *fibrosis*. Since scar tissue is not specialized to perform the functions of the adjacent parenchymal tissue, the fibrosis interferes with normal tissue (parenchymal) function. If collagen repair exceeds its breakdown or loss, a *keloid scar* results. The non-functional scar tissue formed by fibrosis can cause an abnormal and temporary joining of repaired tissues called *adhesions,* These adhesions can be caused by inflammation that persists, improper stitches or a lingering infection.

Figure 7 Wound healing, flow chart

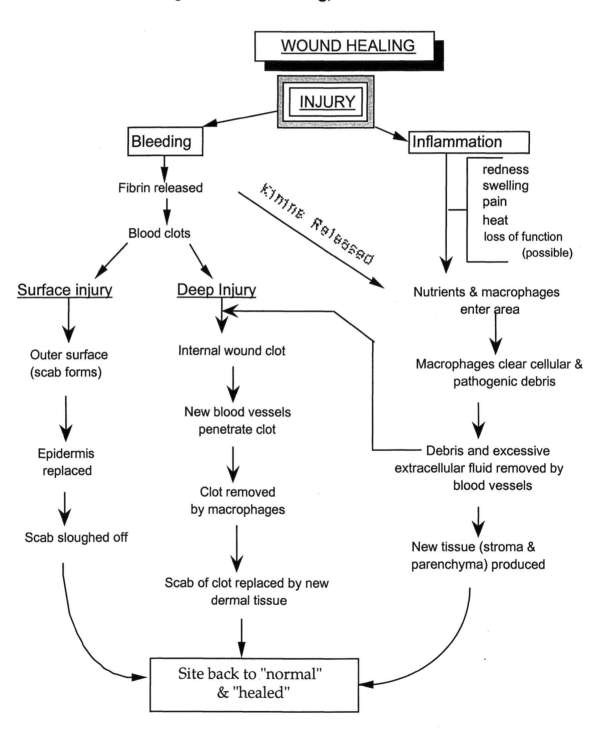

Figure 8 Scar formation flow chart

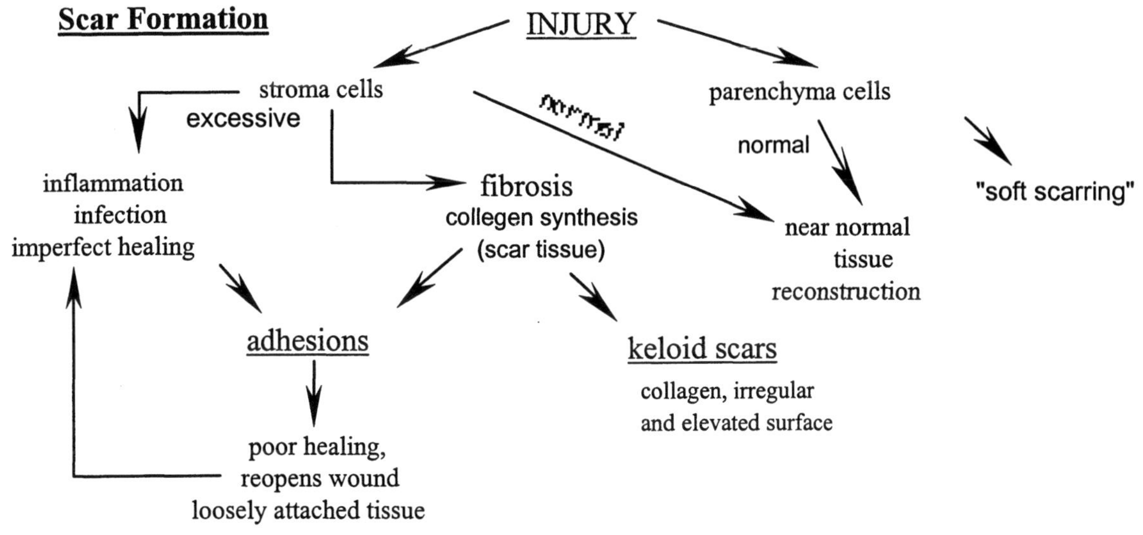

<u>**Scar Formation**</u>   INJURY

stroma cells   parenchyma cells
excessive   *normal*

inflammation   fibrosis   normal
infection   collegen synthesis   near normal
imperfect healing   (scar tissue)   tissue
                              reconstruction   "soft scarring"

adhesions   keloid scars
                              collagen, irregular
poor healing,   and elevated surface
reopens wound
loosely attached tissue

PRACTICE TEST QUESTIONS

1. Epithelial tissue:
   a. covers and lines
   b. secretes and absorbs
   c. receives stimuli
   d. all of the above

2. Epithelia form efficient covering layers because:
   a. they have phagocytic activity
   b. they consist of closely packed cells
   c. they are avascular
   d. they have nerves

3. An epithelial tissue having one layer of cells is:
   a. simple
   b. stratified
   c. columnar
   d. keratinized

4. Mesothelium lines:
   a. blood vessels
   b. true body cavities
   .c. the small intestine
   d. the alveoli of the lungs

5. A primary function of simple squamous epithelium is:
   a. to form a filtration or diffusion membrane
   b. to actively absorb solutes
   c. to move materials by ciliary action
   d. to secrete substances

6. The epithelium lining the urinary bladder and ureters is:
   a. simple cuboidal
   b. stratified squamous
   c. pseudostratified
   d. transitional

7. Connective tissues:
   a. have large amounts of intercellular material
   b. are usually fibrous
   c. protect, support, and connect
   d. all of the above

8. The membrane surrounding cartilage and important in its
      growth is:
   a. periosteum
   b. perichondrium
   c. perineurium
   d. perimysium

9. The cell forming fibers in loose connective tissue is the:
   a. macrophage
   b. mast cell
   c. osteoblast
   d. fibroblast

10. The connective tissue forming the internal framework of many
       body organs is:
   a. elastic tissue
   b. reticular tissue
   c. collagenous tissue
   d. adipose tissue

11. The outer major layer of the skin is the:
   a. hypodermis
   b. dermis
   c. epidermis
   d. corium

12. The layer of skin where skin growth occurs:
   a. prickle-cell layer
   b. granular cell layer
   c. horny layer
   d. germinal layer

13. The dermis:
   a. is vascular connective tissue layer
   b. contains glands
   c. contains sensory corpuscles
   d. all of the above

14. Fat storage occurs in the:
   a. subcutaneous layer
   b. epidermis
   c. corium
   d. dermis

15. A gland of the skin important in temperature regulation is the:
   a. apocrine sweat gland
   b. eccrine sweat gland
   c. sebaceous gland
   d. ceruminous gland

16. Skin color is determined by:
   a. amount of blood within skin
   b. pigment concentrations within skin
   c. oxygenation of blood within skin
   d. all the above

17. Skin thickness is determined by:
   a. genetic factors
   b. mechanical wear and tear
   c. chemical factors
   d. all of the above

Completion

1. The three main layers composing both types of skin are:

2. The epidermis of thick skin contains five sublayers, which are from the deepest to the most superficial:

3. The stratum corneum contains _____ which protects and waterproofs the skin.

4. The _____ layer of the dermis contains Meissner's corpuscles.

5. The panniculus adipose refers to _____.

6. The hair which appears first on the fetal body is known as _____ or _____

7. Skin glands important in the regulation of body temperature are the _____.

8. Decreased resiliency of the skin with aging is due to _____.

9. A pigment known as _____ is primarily responsible for the brown to black skin colors.

10. Yellowish coloration of the skin is due primarily to a pigment known as _____.

11. A tissue is defined as _____.

True and False

1. ____ Classification of epithelium is based on cell shape and arrangement.

2. ____ Compared to epithelia, connective tissues have widely scattered cells.

3. ____ Cartilage is a very vascular connective tissue.

4. ____ Serous membranes are moistened by mucus.

ANSWERS

Multiple Choice
1. d 2. b 3. a 4. b 5. a 6. d 7. d 8. b 9. d
10. b 11. c 12. d 13. d 14 a 15. b 16. d 17. d

Completion
1. epidermis, dermis, subcutaneous
2. stratum basale (germinativum), spinosum, granulosum, lucidum, corneum
3. keratin
4. papillary
5. accumulation of fat in the subcutaneous layer
6. lanugo or down hair
7. eccrine sweat glands
8. loss of elastic fibers in the dermis
9. melanin
10. carotene
11. a group of cells that are similar in structure and function

Osseous Tissue and Bone Structure

(osteology)

Overview

This unit oversees the major functions of the skeletal system, the histology of bone, and intramembranous and endochondral ossification. Bone growth and destruction is used as an example of bone homeostasis. Also included are bone disorders--resulting from some disruption of homeostasis--such as rickets, osteomalacia, osteoporosis, the types of fractures, and the steps involved in fracture repair. Roentgenograms of various bones are used to enhance the structure of bone and its tissues.

Chapter Objectives

1. Describe the functions of the skeletal system.
2. Classify bones according to their shapes and internal organization, and give examples of each type.
3. Identify the cell types in bone, and list their major functions.
4. Compare the structures and functions of compact bone and spongy bone.
5. Compare the mechanisms of intramembranous ossification and endochondral ossification.
6. Discuss the timing of bone development and growth, and account for the differences in the internal structure of the bones of adults.
7. Describe the remodeling and homeostatic mechanisms of the skeletal system.
8. Discuss the effects of nutrition, hormones, exercise, and aging on bone development and on the skeletal system.
9. Describe the types of fractures, and explain how they heal.
10. Identify the major types of bone markings, and explain their functional significance.

Concepts and Definitions

1. The human endoskeleton 1) is the supporting framework of the body, 2) is used by the muscles as levers to cause and strengthen movement, 3) provides protection for body organs, 4) is a reservoir of minerals (cations), 5) contains bone marrow, 6) is a source of nutrients, and 7) is a major center for adult blood cell formation.
2. Compact bone contains osteons (Haversian systems). Spongy bone is composed of interlacing plates or fibers of bone.
3. The structural unit of compact bone is the Haversian system, and the structural unit of spongy bone is a trabecula. The functional unit of both is the osteocyte.
4. Bones 1) have varied shapes, 2) are usually composed of both spongy and compact bone, 3) have articular surfaces covered with fibrous tissue or hyaline cartilage, 4) and grow in width or diameter through the actions of the periosteum.
5. Bones are vascular structures, and show many surface markings that form joints and attachments for muscles.

6. Periosteum is a double layered fibrous connective tissue. The inner layer (osteogenic) on the bone is the layer that functions in bone growth (diameter) and broken bone repair. The outer layer (fibrous layer) is for ligament and tendon attachment to bone.
7. Bone is formed by two processes: a) in a layer of connective tissue, (intramembranous) b) replacement of a skeleton of hyaline cartilage, (intracartilagenous or endochondral)
8. Bone formation, or ossification, starts with osteoblasts that arise from mesenchymal cells.
9. Bone formation takes place in the embryo and within fibrous membranes (intramembranous) and hyaline cartilage (endochondral).
10. The zone of cartilage between the epiphysis and diaphysis of a bone is called the epiphyseal plate. It permits the bone to increase in length until early adulthood.
11. Formation of the epiphyseal line signals the end of bone growth.
12. Remodeling of adult bone is a homeostatic mechanism which new bone is formed by osteoblast activity and old bone is destroyed by osteoclast activity. Both activities are regulated by the STH (somatotropic hormones) also called BGH (body growth hormone).
13. Normal bone growth in the young and bone replacement in an adult depends upon minerals that is, cations (calcium an phosphorus), vitamins (A, C, and D), and hormones (pituitary growth hormones) (STH), sex hormones (testosterone), parathyroid hormones, and thyroid hormones.
14. Bone disorders are the result of a disruption of homeostasis.
15. Bones may be fractured (broken), or suffer infections (e.g., osteomyelitis), deficiency of nutrients (vitamin D), or demineralizing disorders (osteoporosis).
16. Fracture repair involves formation of a fracture hematoma (blood outside of blood vessels), callus formation, and remodeling.
17. Osteoporosis is a disease in which osteoblasts become less active, causing a decrease in bone mass.
18. Paget's disease is characterized by irregular thickening and softening of the bone.
19. Osteomyelitis refers to all infectious diseases of bone that may also involve the periosteum, marrow, and cartilage.
20. A field of scientific research called electrobiology has been used to treat poorly healing fractures. It is now being applied to partial limb regeneration in children and destruction of tumor cells. Electrodes from a low voltage battery pack are implanted into the bone thus accelerating the process of bone repair (intramembranous method).

Summary Outline

I. Functions of the skeletal system:

    A. Support of body-arches of feet, vertebral column, pelvis.
    B. Protect softer tissues-skull, ribs, pelvis.
    C. Movement - act as levers
    D. Hematopoiesis - production of blood cells
    E. Inorganic Salt (mineral) storage - (Ca^{++}, PO_4^-)
    F. Stores adipose tissue
    G. Attachment sites for skeletal muscles

II. Bone Structure

    A. Parts of a long bone (ex. humerus, femur):
        1. diaphysis- shaft region of bone between epiphyses.
        2. epiphysis- the expanded end region.
        3. articular cartilage- layer of hyaline cartilage on the end of the epiphysis.
        4. periosteum- fibrous, vascular bone covering. Provides attachments for tendons and ligaments and is involved in bone development and bone tissue repair

5. <u>endosteum</u>- lines inner surface of compact bone.
6. <u>compact bone</u>- the outer surfaces of the bone are made of this solid, tightly packed tissue. It resists compression and bending.
7. <u>spongy(cancellous) bone</u>- irregular plates of bone found inside the compact bone. Reduces the weight of the skeleton.
8. <u>medullary cavity</u>- cavity in the diaphysis.
9. <u>yellow bone marrow</u> - found in medullary cavity - fat storage
10. <u>red bone marrow</u>- where hematopoiesis occurs. found in the spaces between bony plates of the spongy bone.

III. Bone Development and Growth
  A. <u>Intramembranous bone formation</u>
     1. sheet like masses of connective tissue [CT] form in embryo
     2. osteoblasts form in between the sheets of CT
     3. osteoblasts begin to lay down bony material around themselves.
     4. spongy bone is produced between the membranes.
     5. the sheet like membranes persist to become the periosteum.
     6. osteoblasts on the inner surface of the periosteum lay down compact bone over the spongy bone which was formed between the membranes.
  B. <u>Endochondral bone formation</u>
     1. formation of a hyaline cartilaginous model.
     2. a. periosteum starts to develop around model.
         b. primary ossification center begins in middle of model.
     3. a. formation of compact bony collar around model.
         b. beginning of medullary cavity as blood vessels grow into the area.
         c. secondary ossification begins at the ends of the model.
     4. cartilage cells in the epiphyseal disk undergo mitosis which results in increase in bone length.
     5. primary & secondary ossification centers overtake disk and bone becomes completely ossified.
  C. <u>Factors affecting bone growth</u>
     1. Nutrition - Vitamin A - necessary for bone reabsorption
         Vitamin C - needed for proper collagen synthesis
         Vitamin D - needed for proper absorption of calcium from gut
     2. Physical Exercise (stress) - stimulates bone growth
     3. Hormones- Thyroid Hormones - can cause premature ossification
         Sex Hormones - stimulates growth and ossification
         Growth Hormone (GH) - stimulates epiphyseal disk growth.
              excessive GH in children - pituitary gigantism
              excessive GH in adults - acromegaly
              insufficient GH in children - pituitary dwarfism

IV. Bone Fractures / Bone Repair
  A. <u>Types of Fractures</u>
  1. Simple fracture -   a complete fracture that does not penetrate through the skin
  2. Compound fracture - a complete fracture that breaks through the skin.
  3. Comminuted fracture - a complete fracture with many fracture pieces.
  4. Greenstick fracture - an incomplete fracture that starts out transverse.

B. Steps to Fracture Repair
    1. Fracture Hematoma
    2. Fibrocartilaginous Callus
    3. Bony Callus
    4. Bone Remodeling

V. Blood Calcium Homeostasis (hormone controlled)

Normal blood calcium levels = 9 to 11mg/ 100ml of blood
Blood calcium levels above 11 = Hypercalcemia
Blood calcium levels below 9 = Hypocalcemia
Hormones involved:
1. Calcitonin - released by thyroid gland when blood calcium levels are high
    Function: decreases blood calcium levels by
    a. stimulating osteoblasts to form bone tissue.
    b. inhibiting osteoclast activity
2. Parathyroid Hormone (PTH) - released by parathyroid glands when blood calcium levels are low.
    Function: increases blood calcium levels by
    a. stimulating osteoclast activity
    b. inhibiting osteoblast activity
    c. stimulates calcium absorption from gut
    d. causes kidneys to conserve calcium.

So, we can see that the homeostasis of blood calcium is maintained by the opposing effects of these two hormones. Keep in mind, it is not a situation in which one is secreted while the other one is not secreted, but rather by increasing or decreasing the amounts secreted beyond normal levels!

Practice TEST QUESTIONS

1. The human skeleton:
    a. repairs itself
    b. is an active metabolic tissue
    c. provides support and protection
    c. all of the above

2. Cranial bones develop:
    a. from cartilage
    b. in a membrane
    c. from a tendon
    d. from skin

3. An exaggerated curvature of the lumbar spine is:
    a. lordosis
    b. scoliosis
    c. kyphosis
    d. ankylosis

4. Bone growth in diameter is typical of the
    a. intramembranous method
    b. endochondral method
    c. osteogenic method
    d. cephla-caudal method

5. The cell that forms bone is the:
    a. osteocyte
    b. osteoclast
    c. osteoblast
    d. chondrocyte

6. The periosteum
    a. encircles the outside of bone
    b. encircles the inside of bone
    c. stops growing when bone length stops growing
    d. is important for the final length of a bone.

COMPLETION

1. Name 4 functions of the skeleton.

2. Name and summarize the two types of bone growth:

3. Steps in the healing of a fracture include:

4. The 5 parts of an osteon are:

ANSWERS

Multiple Choice
1. e 2. b 3. a 4. a 5. c 6. a
Completion
1. protection, storage of calcium and phosphate, attachment for muscles, hematopoiesis, support, etc.
2. intramembranous and endochondral, (refer to your lecture notes and reading)
3. formation of binding tissue, granulation tissue formation, callus formation.
4. Haversian canal, lamellae, lacunae, osteocytes, canaliculi.

Articulations/Joints

Overview

Our body movements must conform to the limitations of the human body. For example, it is not possible to bend the shaft of the humerus or femur; movements are restricted to joints, where bones articulate. The same is true of artificial limbs, which use mechanical equivalents of human joints. Very early in life, we learn to work within those limitations. Each joint—natural or artificial—will tolerate a specific range of motion. A variety of bony surfaces, cartilages, ligaments, tendons, and muscles—or metal and plastic balls, shafts, and screws—work together to keep movement within the normal range. The stronger the joint, the more restrictive the limitations are likely to be. In this chapter, we will examine representative joints and explore the relationship between structural stability and the range of motion.

Chapter Objectives

1. Contrast the major categories of joints, and explain the relationship between structure and function for each category.
2. Describe the basic structure of a synovial joint, identifying possible accessory structures and their functions.
3. Describe the dynamic movements of the skeleton.
4. List the types of synovial joints, and discuss how the characteristic motions of each type are related to its anatomical structure.
5. Describe the articulations between the vertebrae of the vertebral column.
6. Describe the structure and function of the shoulder, elbow, hip, and knee joints.
7. Explain the relationship between joint strength and mobility, using specific examples.

Concepts and Definitions

1. An articulation (joint) is a region of contact between bones.
2. Fibrous joints, that is, sutures and syndesmoses are held together by fibrous connective tissue and allow little or no movement.
3. Cartilaginous joints, that is, synchondroses and symphyses are held together by cartilage and thus allow little or no movement.
4. A synovial joint (diarthritic joint) is characterized by a synovial cavity, articular cartilage, and an articular capsule. The capsule consists of an outer layer, the fibrous capsule (joint ligaments), and an inner layer, the synovial membrane. Many synovial joints also contain accessory ligaments, articular discs, and bursae.
5. The presence of the synovial cavity permits free movement; however the movement is limited by the adjacent soft parts, tension of ligaments, and muscle tension.

6. The principal movements that occur at synovial joints are gliding, angular (flexion, extension, dorsiflexion, hyperextension, plantar flexion, abduction, and adduction), rotation, circumduction, and special (inversion, eversion, protraction, retraction, supination, and pronation).

7. Subtypes of synovial joints include gliding, hinge, pivot, ellipsoidal, saddle, and ball-and-socket.

8. Septic arthritis is caused by the invasion of an infectious agent into the synovial-lined joint space.

9. The many types of arthritis are classified according to specific clinical symptoms.

10. Bursa are connective tissue sacs filled with synovial fluid that reduce friction. If they become inflamed, the condition is called bursitis.

11. Tendonitis frequently occurs as inflammation involving the tendon sheaths and synovial membrane that surrounds joints.

12. A dislocation is the displacement of a bone from a joint, while a sprain is the forcible wrenching or twisting of a joint with partial rupture or other injury to its attachments.

13. Slipped intervertebral discs usually exert abnormal pressure on the spinal nerves causing considerable, sometimes very acute, pain.

Summary Outline

I. Definition of a joint-point of connection between two or more bones.

II. Classification of joints
A. functional:
    1. immovable
    2. slightly movable
    3. freely movable
B. structural
    1. fibrous-no synovial cavity, held together by fibrous connective tissue.
       -permit little or no movement
       ex. sutures of skull
    2. cartilaginous- no synovial cavity, held together by cartilage.
       -allow little or no movement.
           ex. pubic symphysis and between bodies of vertebrae
    3. synovial-has synovial cavity, has articular capsule and ligaments.
        -freely movable
       a. *structure of synovial joints*
          i. articular cartilage(hyaline)
          ii. articular capsule
           two layers-inner synovial membrane
           -outer fibrous capsule
          iii. ligaments
          iv. synovial fluid-secreted by synovial membrane.
           -lubrication, nourishes cartilage
          v. bursae-fluid filled sacs which decrease friction between:
            skin and bone(knee, elbow)
            tendons and bone
            muscles and bone
            ligaments and bone
       b. *types of synovial joints*
          i. gliding joints-side to side movement.
            example: intercarpal joints.
          ii. hinge joints-allow flexion/extension.
            example: elbow, knee

iii. <u>pivot joints</u>-allows rotation.
   example: atlas/axis, proximal radioulnar.
iv. <u>ball and socket</u>-ball on one bone fits into a depression on another bone.
   example: shoulder, hip.

III. Joint Pathology

A. <u>Arthritis</u>-inflammation of one or more joints.
   1. rheumatoid arthritis-autoimmune disease
      -cartilage and joint lining are damaged
      -bilateral
   2. osteoarthritis-caused by aging, irritation, wear and tear.
      -articular cartilage is worn away and replaced with bone spurs
   3. gout-sodium urate crystals are deposited in the joints.
      -crystals irritate the joints causing pain, inflammation and swelling
B. <u>Bursitis</u>-inflammation of a bursa.
      -caused by trauma, infection, overuse and misuse.
C. <u>Dislocation</u>-displacement of a bone from a joint in which ligaments,
      -the capsule and tendons are damaged.
D. <u>Sprain</u>-partial or complete tearing of the ligaments and the capsule of a joint.
      note: strain-tearing of a muscle not the joint.

Movements

flexion/extension
abduction/adduction
medial rotation/lateral rotation
inversion/eversion
dorsiflexion/plantar flexion
dorsi extension/plantar extension
supination/pronation
protraction/retraction
elevation/depression

Muscle Tissue/Myology

Chapter Objectives

1. Describe the characteristics and functions of skeletal muscle tissue.
2. Describe the organization of muscle at the tissue level.
3. Explain the unique characteristics of skeletal muscle fibers.
4. Identify the structural components of a sarcomere.
5. Identify the components of the neuromuscular junction and summarize the events involved in the neural control of skeletal muscles.
6. Explain the key steps involved in the contraction of a skeletal muscle fiber.
7. Describe the changes in length of muscle during contraction and relaxation.
8. Compare the types of muscle contractions.
9. Describe the mechanisms by which muscle fibers obtain the energy to power contractions.
10. Relate the types of muscle fibers to muscle performance.
11. Distinguish between aerobic and anaerobic endurance, and explain their implications for muscular performance.
12. Describe a muscle's origin and insertion.
13. Describe the changes that occur in muscles throughout one's life span.
14. Describe the effects of aging on muscles.
15. Give examples of interactions between the muscular system and each of the other organ systems.
16. Identify the structural and functional differences among skeletal, cardiac, and smooth muscle cells.
17. Discuss the role that smooth muscle tissue plays in systems throughout the body.

Concepts and Definitions

I. The major characteristics of muscle tissue are: *irritability*, *contractility*, *extensibility*, and *elasticity*.
2. Based on its histology and function, all muscle tissue is classified as: (a) skeletal or striated voluntary muscle; (b) cardiac or striated involuntary muscle; or (c) smooth or visceral involuntary muscle.
3. All muscle exhibit a common contractile unit [sarcomere] utilizing ATP and composed of the proteins actin, myosin.
4. Fibrous connective tissue components associated with skeletal muscle are epimysium, perimysium, endomysium, tendons, and aponeuroses.
5. The energy for muscular contraction is supplied by adenosine triphosphate [ATP] and creatine phosphate [CP].
6. The motor unit is the basic nerve-muscle unit in contraction.
7. According to the sliding filament hypothesis, a muscle fiber contracts when its sarcomere's cross-bridges between the actin and myosin myofilaments shorten.
8. According to the all-or-none principle, muscle fibers will contract to their fullest extent or not a all.
9. The principal types of muscle contractions are isotonic, isometric, tonic, twitch, tetanic, and treppe.
10. A typical myogram of a twitch contraction consists of a latent period, contraction period, force of contraction and relaxation period.

11. Muscular hypertrophy refers to an increase in the diameter of each muscle fiber resulting from excessive but forceful muscular activity. The cause can be from reduced blood flow during times of excessive contraction.

12. Fast (white) muscle fibers have an extensive sarcoplasmic reticulum for the rapid release and uptake of calcium ions needed for rapid contractions, have fewer capillaries and less myoglobin and therefore fatigue rapidly. One example is an external eye muscle.

13. Slow (red) muscle fibers are thinner fibers, have more blood capillaries, more myoglobin and a less extensive sarcoplasmic reticulum and takes a long time to fatigue. An example is the gastrocnemius.

14. Muscle tissue helps to maintain the homeostasis of the body. Examples include oxygen debt, fatigue, and heat production.

15. **Muscle fatigue** results from the diminished availability of oxygen and the toxic effects of lactic acid and carbon dioxide accumulated during exercise. This is referred to as the anaerobic phase of contraction.

16. *Skeletal muscle fibers* are multinuclear and cylindrical, rapidly contracting, innervated by nerves, and utilize protein [actin & myosin] myofilaments as their contractile units.

17. *Smooth muscle fibers* consists of uninuclear spindle shaped fibers most commonly found aggregated in sheets around hollow contracting organs such as intestines or blood vessels.

18. Unitary smooth muscle behaves like one mass, and is found in the digestive tract and reproductive systems. Multi-unit smooth muscle is innervated by nerves and can alter its strength of contraction. An example of this is the iris of the eye. Single smooth muscle fibers or small units from the middle layer of blood vessels contract due to nervous system innervation, temperature and chemicals within the blood. This results in vasoconstriction.

19. A variety of relationships between muscle length, tension and contraction are summarized within the chapter, as are the energy sources for contractions, and heat relationships.

20. Pain, tenderness, and stiffness of joints and muscles in the thigh is called "charleyhorse."

21. A variety of disorders affecting skeletal muscle occur, including atrophy, dystrophy, myasthenia gravis, and paralysis. Muscle cramps, spasms, and fatigue are related to lactic acid and oxygen levels within the muscle fibers. 22. Abnormal muscular contractions include spasms, cramps, convulsions, tetany, fibrillations, and tics.

23. Muscular dystrophy is characterized by degeneration of muscle cells that lead to progressive atrophy. This increases the levels of the CPK enzyme (creatinine phosphokinase) in blood and is used to diagnose dystrophy and other wasting diseases of muscle.

24. Myasthenia gravis may be treated by anticholinesterase drugs, steroid drugs, and plasmatheresis.

Summary Outline

Skeletal muscle has the properties of irritability, contractility, extensibility, and elasticity. It makes up the muscular system and constitutes 40 to 50 percent of body weight.

Skeletal muscle is attached to bone by a dense connective tissue called a tendon

A. CONNECTIVE TISSUE AND MUSCLE TISSUE WITHIN MUSCLE
   1. Looser type of collagenous connective tissue extends into and surrounds all muscle fibers making up whole muscle.
   2. Blood vessels and nerves ramify through connective tissue
      a. Epimysium-surrounds whole muscle
      b. Perimysium-surrounds bundles of muscle fibers; these bundles called fascicles
      c. Endomysium-surrounds individual muscles fibers

B. NERVE SUPPLY TO MUSCLES
1. Muscles supplied with sensory and motor nerves
2. Sensory nerves convey to the central nervous system the state of contraction of the muscle
3. Motor nerves convey impulses from the somatic division of the central nervous system to muscles and control their contraction
   a. Motor unit is the single motor nerve and the bundle of muscle fibers it supplies
   b. Area where motor nerve ending meets muscle called neuromuscular junction (motor end plate, myoneural junction)

C. STRUCTURE OF A NEUROMUSCULAR JUNCTION
1. Nerve terminal oval to round structure; rests in specialized region of muscle membrane that is highly enfolded, called subneural clefts
   (synaptic folds, subneural apparatus)
2. Nerve terminal contains mitochondria, few filaments and microtubules, and many synaptic vesicles that contain acetylcholine
3. Acetylcholine released on stimulation of nerve; this causes muscle to contract if threshold is crossed or exceeded
4. Action of acetylcholine blocked by enzyme acetylcholinesterase, which is located at end plate region
5. Some synapses will reuptake the synaptic mediator into the presynaptic structure instead of destroying it by an enzyme.

D. ULTRASTRUCTURE OF MUSCLE
1. Each individual muscle fiber made up of many smaller myofibrils
2. Myofibrils made up of many myofilaments [contractile proteins]
3. Two types of myofilaments: actin and myosin
4. Arrangement of myofilaments gives rise to banding pattern seen in "striated" muscle
   A-band I-band   H-band Z-line
   Sarcomere-region between two Z-lines; the functional unit of all muscle fibers.

E. MUSCLE CONTRACTION CONCEPT AND SEQUENCE
1. Sliding-filament hypothesis-change in relative length of I-and H-band and sarcomere when muscle, at rest, shortens, and is stretched
2. Interaction of actin and myosin at cross bridges of myosin filaments; process that requires ATP
3. Actin-myosin interaction requires calcium
4. Troponin and tropomyosin-regulator proteins present in actin filament
5. Troponin is receptive protein for calcium
6. Calcium stored in longitudinal elements of sarcoplasmic reticulum

F. THE STIMULUS
1. Minimal stimulus-weakest stimulus to excite some motor units
2. Subminimal stimulus-a stimulus with a value just below that of a minimal stimulus
3. Maximal stimulus-excites all motor units
4. Absolute refractory period-brief interval of time immediately following a contraction when no stimulus will cause contraction
5. Relative refractory period-interval of depressed excitability

G. MECHANICS OF MUSCLE CONTRACTION
1. All-or-none law-stimulus to a single muscle fiber will cause a maximal response or none at all
2. Twitch response-contraction of muscle seen following a single maximal stimulus to either nerve or muscle-latent period; period of contraction; period of relaxation
3. Isotonic contraction (twitch)-length changes, tension remains the same
4. Isometric contraction (twitch)-same length, but tension changes
5. Summation-a greater magnitude of tension or shortening due to rapid succession of 2 to 3 stimuli
6. Tetanus-greatest magnitude of response, usually 3 to 4 times greater than twitch response; results from repetitive stimulation at a rate that maintains sustained maximal summation.
7. Tonus - a continual level of some degree of contraction of all muscles that gives a certain firmness and maintains a slight, steady pull on bony attachments

H. SOURCES OF ENERGY FOR MUSCLE CONTRACTION
1. Source of energy is ATP
2. Means of providing continual supply of ATP
   a. Creatine phosphate
   b. Glycolysis
   d. Oxidative phosphorylation (citric acid or Krebs cycle)
   e. ATP
3. Muscle fatigue due to accumulation of lactic acid, muscle in oxygen debt

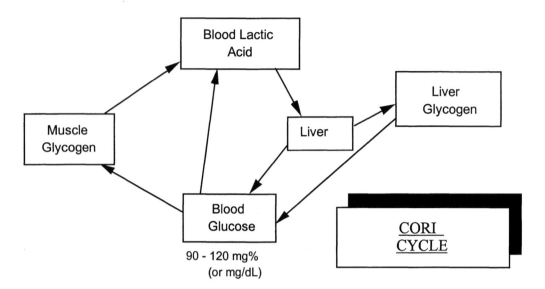

Figure 9 Cori cycle, flow chart

Summary Outline

I. Functions of muscular system
    A. movement of skeleton(body)
    B. maintenance of posture
    C. movement of food, fluids
    D. heat production

II. Structure of a skeletal muscle
    A. <u>Connective tissue coverings</u> (CT):
       1. <u>endomysium</u>- CT that covers each individual muscle fiber.
       2. <u>perimysium</u>- CT that surrounds bundles of muscle fibers (<u>fasciculi</u>)
       3. <u>epimysium</u> (deep fascia)- CT which surrounds an entire skeletal muscle.
       4. <u>fascia</u>- CT which holds groups of skeletal muscles together. example: quadriceps
    B. <u>Parts of skeletal muscle fibers</u>: (a muscle fiber = muscle cell)
       1. <u>sarcolemma</u>- the cell membrane of a muscle cell.
       2. <u>sarcoplasm</u>- the cytoplasm of a muscle cell. There are numerous nuclei, and mitochondria in a muscle cell.
       3. <u>myofibrils</u>-   each muscle cell is made up of numerous myofibrils.
         - made of two proteins as *<u>myofilaments</u>*:
       4. <u>sarcoplasmic reticulum</u>- stores calcium after actively transporting it in from the sarcoplasm. Has expanded regions called <u>cisternae</u>.
       5. <u>transverse tubules</u>- in folds of the sarcolemma which extend all the way through the muscle fiber. These tubules are continuous with the interstitial fluid.
    C. <u>Myofilament Structure</u>
    Two Types;
       1. <u>thick filaments</u> - made up of the protein **myosin**

2. <u>thin filaments</u> - made up of the following proteins;
      a. actin
      b. tropomyosin
      c. troponin

III. Neuromuscular junction (NMJ) the point at which an axon from a <u>motor neuron</u> communicates with the sarcolemma of a muscle cell.
   A. .<u>motor end plate</u>- a highly folded area of sarcolemma at the site of the neuromuscular junction.
   B. <u>synaptic cleft</u> - the space between the axon terminal bulb and the motor end plate.
   C. <u>synaptic vesicles</u> - membrane sacs located in the terminal bulbs.
     - The neurotransmitter, *Acetylcholine (Ach)* is used in the NMJ.
   <u>Muscle relaxation</u>:
     1. nerve impulse ceases
     2. ACh is broken down at the synapse by *cholinesterase*. This prevents a single impulse from causing a continued contraction.
     3. a Ca^{++} pump in the sarcoplasmic reticulum(SR) quickly pumps Ca back into the SR
     4. the <u>troponin-tropomyosin complex</u> moves back in between the actin and myosin myofilaments
     5. the cross bridges are broken
     6. muscle relaxation occurs.

IV. Motor unit- is composed of a single *motor neuron* and all the muscle fibers which it forms junctions with.
Note: Some areas of the body where a great degree of muscle coordination is required will have only a few myofibrils per motor neuron (ex: external eye muscles). Conversely, a muscle which is involved in powerful movements will have numerous myofibrils per motor neuron (ex: thigh muscles).

V. Clinical applications:
  1. *Clostridium botulinum* (<u>Botulism</u>), a bacterium that grows in improperly canned foods, secretes <u>botulinus toxin</u>. This toxin *prevents the release of ACh* from motor nerve fibers. Skeletal muscle fibers are unable to contract. The diaphragm is made of skeletal muscle, breathing stops and death ensues.

  2. **Disuse Atrophy**: a decreased size and strength of muscle fibers due to a lack of movements against resistance. The number of fibers (cells) remains the same, but the number of filaments per fiber decreases. Causes include immobilization, chronic illness, denervation.

  3. **Muscular dystrophy** (MD):term applied to a number of *genetic disorders* that produce progressive deterioration of skeletal muscles because of mixed cell hypertrophy(adipose), atrophy(muscle), and necrosis. Primarily a disease of muscle in that the nervous system is not involved.
     Muscle tissues die and replaced by fat and CT. There is a false hypertrophy(*pseudohypertrophy*) with muscle weakness.
   The disease is progressive. There is no cure for any of the muscular dystrophies.

     Duchene's MD-most common type. <u>Inherited</u> as gene defect on the <u>X-chromosome</u>. Postural muscles of the hip and shoulder are affected first. At about 3 years of age frequent falling is a common first symptom. Wheelchairs are necessary at about nine years and *death* due to *cardiorespiratory failure* usually occurs in young adulthood.

4. **Myasthenia gravis**: a disorder of transmission at the NMJ thought to result from a decrease in ACh receptor sites at the NMJ due to an autoimmune response. The disease may progress from eye muscle weakness to generalized body weakness.

5. **Muscular hypertrophy**-an increase in the *size of muscle fibers* in response to an increase in activity. The muscle grows larger when exercised with heavy weights or resistance. The strength of a muscle is directly proportional to the cross-sectional area or diameter of the muscle.

6. **Drugs which affect the NMJ** :
   a. **curare**-prevents depolarization at the motor end plate. Used in surgery to prevent reflex contraction of muscles during surgery.
   b. **physostigmine / neostigmine**-inhibit acetylcholinesterase, thereby allowing ACH to accumulate. Used in Rx of myasthenia gravis.

IV. Energy sources for muscle contraction:
A. Adenosine triphosphate(ATP)-mitochondrion supplies most ATP.
   Myosin filaments contain ATPase, an enzyme which causes this reaction:
   ATP ----> ADP+ P+ energy.
B. Creatine phosphate(CP) regenerates ATP from ADP and P:
   ATP + CP----> ATP + Creatine
   -only enough CP and ATP to last for about 15 seconds.
C. When lots of ATP is present in a cell, energy is *stored in CP* molecule.
   -During cellular activity as ATP is used up, ADP concentrations increase and CP is used to reconvert ADP back into ATP.
   -CP is used up rapidly and the cell needs its ATP to be supplied by glycolysis, the Kreb's cycle and the ETS.
   Hemoglobin-the molecule which transports O_2 & CO_2 in the blood.
   Myoglobin-molecule in muscle cells which stores O_2 (gives most of the red color of muscle).
D. Oxygen debt: after strenuous exercise accumulated *lactic acid* is converted to glucose in the liver, muscle cells need to resupply themselves with ATP and CP. The O_2 debt is the amount of O_2 needed after a strenuous activity to perform these conversions.
E. Muscle fatigue: is usually the result of an inadequate supply of O_2, a depletion of glycogen and an accumulation of lactic acid. Muscle cramps are due to lack of ATP needed to pump Ca^{+2} back into the sarcoplasmic reticulum, the muscle is in a partially tetanic contraction.
   Clinical application: Rigor mortis: result of a lack of ATP. This prevents relaxation thus the muscle stays contracted.
F. Heat production: about 1/3 of the energy released by cellular respiration is lost as heat. This heat is important in maintaining body temperature, but when excessive must be released.

V. Muscular Responses:
A. *Threshold stimulus*-the minimal strength of an electrical stimulus which will result in a muscular contraction.
B. *All-or-none response*-when a muscle cell(fiber) is exposed to a threshold or greater stimulus it contracts completely. There are *no partial contractions of muscle cells.*

C. *Recruitment of motor units*-a motor unit consists of a *motor neuron* and all the *muscle fibers* it supplies. A motor unit will respond in an *all-or-none* fashion. A whole muscle doesn't act this way because it is made up of many different motor units, supplied by different motor neurons. As an increase in strength is needed more motor units are stimulated in a process called recruitment.

D. *Twitch contraction*-a brief muscle contraction which is followed immediately by relaxation. Demonstrated in the lab by removing a muscle from an animal and attaching it to a myograph, then stimulating it to a greater than threshold stimulus.
   Stages of a muscle twitch:
   1st. latent period-time between stimulus and beginning of contraction.
   2nd. period of contraction
   3rd. period of relaxation

E. Types of *sustained contractions*:(occur when a muscle is exposed to a series of stimuli and complete relaxation is not allowed.)
   1. treppe-an increase in the strength of contraction of a muscle when it is exposed to a series of stimuli.
   2. tetanic contraction -a sustained contraction which lacks relaxation.
   3. muscle tone-the tension present in a muscle that is at rest. Sustained contractions of muscle which are necessary for balance, posture.

VII. Smooth muscle:
   1. elongate with tapered ends
   2. contain actin, myosin filaments which extend length of cell.
   3. lacks striations
   4. two types:
      a. *multiunit smooth muscle*-are less well organized and occur as separate fibers. Located in eyes(iris), walls of blood vessels.
         Contracts after motor nerve impulse.
      b. *visceral smooth muscle*-composed of sheets of spindle shaped cells which are attached to one another. Found in walls of organs of GI tract, uterus, urinary bladder.
         1. capable of stimulating one another
         2. exhibit *rhythmicity*, pattern of repeated contractions
   5. are stimulated by ACh and norepinephrine (NE)
   6. are slower to contract and slower to relax than skeletal muscle.

VIII. Cardiac muscle-Characteristics
   1. found only in heart
   2. *striated* cells attached end to end to form fibers.
   3. cells are interconnected to form networks
   4. well developed sarcoplasmic reticulum, numerous mitochondria.
   5. cells are connected by *intercalated disks*. These hold adjacent cells together, transmit force of contraction, and allow for nerve impulses to move rapidly between cardiac muscle cells.
   6. self-exciting

Medications that alter muscle contractions

Contraction of the three types is regulated by the nervous system, although, visceral and cardiac can contract spontaneously by leaking Ca^{+2} ions, medications and poisons. Normally, sensory nerves receive and transmit to the appropriate areas in the brain the condition of a muscle. Motor nerves will then send impulses to the muscles for needed contractions. Many motor nerves will innervate a muscle. A **motor unit** is a single motor neuron and all of the muscle fibers it stimulates. The fewer the number of fibers in a motor unit the more rapid and skilled its movements will become. External eye muscles with 12 muscle fibers per unit used to follow a moving object are a good example. However, if the one motor unit has 300 fibers the motion is slower and coarse. Muscles that give posture as one prime example of slower contracting muscles. The region where a motor neuron terminates at muscle fibers is called the motor end plate, neuromuscular junction or myoneural junction. Study the anatomy of this motor end plate as explained in your lecture text book.

SYNAPTIC CHEMISTRY

The chemistry of synapses within the brain creates our existence, consciousness and ultimately the personality. Read your text book and refer to the lecture notes to understand its basic activity.

DRUGS ASSOCIATED WITH MUSCLES

Trade Name: Botox
Generic Name: botulinus toxin
Action: paralysis of respiratory muscles
Physiology: prevents the release of ACh

Trade Name: Malathion (an insecticide)
Generic Name: organophosphorous
Action: paralyzes
Physiology: inhibit AChase activity thus causing extensive contractions (antitoxin: atropine)

Trade Name: Tubocurarine chloride
Generic Name: curare
Action: nondepolarizing muscle relaxant resulting in paralysis
Physiology: binds to ACh receptor therefore blocking impulses

Trade Name: Calin & Isoptin   a calcium channel blocker
Generic Name: verapamil
Action: weakens muscle contraction
Physiology: blocks calcium release from sarcotubular system to reduce coronary artery spasms
(angina) or prolonged spasms (heart attacks)

Trade Name: Procardia & Adalat a calcium channel blocker
Generic Name: nifedipine   a calcium channel blocker
Action: weakens muscle contraction
Physiology: blocks calcium release from sarcotubular system to reduce coronary artery spasms
(heart attacks)

Figure 10 Disorders of skeletal muscle, table

Disorder	Probable Causes	Symptoms	Outcomes
fibrosis	Injury or degeneration of muscle fibers (cells), which are replaced by fibrous connective tissue or scar tissue	Stiffness	Impairment of function
fibrositis	inflammation of fibrous tissue; in lumbar region, called lumbago; may follow injury or muscle strain	stiffness and soreness of connective tissue of muscle	not progressive or destructive; may disappear and recur
myositis	inflammation of muscle cells	swelling, pain, usually in shoulders and arms	depends on the cause of the ailment
muscular dystrophy	hereditary	degeneration of muscle cells; bilateral; leads to atrophy and crippling	no known cure as of yet
myasthenia gravis (MG)	a failure of transmission over motor end plates; may be hereditary; more common in females	muscle weakness; easily fatigued; facial muscles sag; difficulty in speaking and swallowing; limb muscles may be involved	progressive
paralysis	failure in motor neurons to muscles	muscles cannot contract; atrophy follows	duration depends on the cause
spastic paralysis	damage to motor tracts of brain and spinal cord (upper motor neurons)	muscles in constant contracted state	duration depends on the cause
flaccid paralysis	damage to motor nerves (lower motor neurons) in cranial and spinal nerves	muscles in a constant relaxed state	duration depends on the cause
tremor	indicates possible damage	involuntary, repetitive contractions	usually transient and duration depends on the cause
spasm	usually chemical, electrolyte imbalances, toxins (ex. tetanus)	forcible, painful contraction, involuntary and of short duration	massage helps to increase blood flow, also correct the cause
cramp	overuse of muscles, causing accumulation of muscle stimulation chemicals, increased reflex responses	painful, involuntary contraction of muscles	transitory; may be helped by stretching the body part or voluntary contraction of the antagonist muscle

practice TEST QUESTIONS

1. The functional unit of skeletal muscle structure is the:
   a. fiber
   b. fibril
   c. myoblast
   d. mesoderm
2. The sarcoplasm is the :
   a. membrane of the fiber
   b. contractile unit of the fiber
   c. cytoplasm of the fiber
   d. connective tissue holding the fibers together
3. The contractile proteins of muscle are:
   a. myosin
   b. actin
   c. creatine phosphate
   d. glucose
4. A cation necessary for contraction to occur is:
   a. ammonium
   b. sodium
   c. potassium
   d. calcium

5. Energy sources used to sustain muscular contraction include:
   a. phosphocreatine
   b. glucose
   c. fatty acids
   d. all of the above
6. A sustained partial contraction of a muscle is called:
   a. a twitch
   b. tone
   c. treppe
   d. a cramp
7. The nerves to skeletal muscle originate from the:
   a. somatic division of the peripheral nervous system
   b. autonomic division of the peripheral nervous system
   c. visceral efferent fibers of peripheral nervous system
   d. none of the above
8. Unitary smooth muscle:
   a. exhibits spontaneous depolarization
   b. does not depend on nerves to contract
   c. is located within the walls of the intestines
   d. all of the above

TRUE AND FALSE

1. ____ Nerves are essential to the maintenance of the muscle tone.
2. ____ Acetylcholine causes muscle depolarization.
3. ____ Perimysium surrounds muscle fibers.
4. ____ Thin filaments shorten and are composed of myosin.
5. ____ Isometric contraction occurs when no movement is allowed.
6. ____ Glucose combined with oxygen is then broken down to synthesize ATP for contraction.
7. ____ A muscle twitch demonstrates the phases of muscle activity.
8. ____ Multiunit smooth muscle may respond to reflex stimulation.

COMPLETION

1.   Four chemicals necessary for muscle contraction are:

2.   Four properties of skeletal muscle include:

3.   The term _____ is given to the time interval between muscle stimulation and the beginning of contraction.

4.   Myosin as an enzyme splits _____.

5.   "Warming-up" a muscle results in _____

_____

ANSWERS

Multiple Choice
1.a, 2.c, 3.a & b, 4.d, 5.d, 6.b, 7.a, 8.d
TRUE and FALSE
1. true, 2. true, 3. false, 4. false, 5. true, 6. false, 7. true, 8. true
Completion
1. myosin, actin, calcium, ATP
2. contractility, elasticity, excitability, conductivity
3. latent period
4. ATP to release energy for contraction
5. more energy being directed toward contraction and more efficient contractions.

Chapter 10 Muscle tissue [myology]

Neural tissue/Neurology

Overview

A fter the nervous system is classified into its major anatomical subdivisions, the histology of neuroglia and neurons is considered. Physiological aspects of nervous tissue discussed are regeneration, impulse initiative and transmission, the all-or-none principles, saltatory transmission, speed of nerve impulses, impulse conduction across synapses, excitatory synaptic transmission, inhibitory synaptic transmission, and transmitter substances. Factors that affect impulse transmissions and the organization of neuronal synapses are also treated.

Chapter Objectives

1. List the two major anatomical divisions of the nervous system, and describe the characteristics of each division.
2. Describe the structure and function of the nervous system.
3. Sketch and label the structure of a typical neuron, and describe the functions of each component.
4. Classify neurons on the basis of their structure and function.
5. Describe the locations and functions of neuroglia.
6. Explain how the resting potential is created and maintained.
7. Describe the events involved in the generation and propagation of an action potential.
8. Discuss the factors that affect the speed with which action potentials are propagated.
9. Describe the structure of a synapse, and explain the mechanism involved in synaptic activity.
10. Describe the major types of neurotransmitters and neuromodulators, and discuss their effects on postsynaptic membranes.
11. Discuss the interactions that make possible the processing of information in neural tissue.
12. Describe the patterns of interaction between neurons that are involved in the processing of information at higher levels.
13. Give examples of interactions between the nervous system and each of the other organ systems.

Concepts and Definitions

1. The nerve impulse is the body's quickest method for maintaining system homeostasis and organ control.
2. The nervous system is derived from embryonic ectoderm, and is the FIRST of all the body systems to develop.
3. The nervous system 1)detects changes, 2)interprets 3)analyses senses, remembers information, and 4) then controls organ and chemical response to maintain homeostasis.

4. The nervous system is divided into two principal divisions: central and peripheral; the latter divided into somatic and autonomic divisions.

5. The histology of the nervous system consists of neurons and neuroglia (glial cells).

6. Neuroglia physically support and protect chemically neurons which conduct nerve impulses.

7. Neurons 1) are the structural and functional units of the system 2) are highly excitable and conductible, 3) exhibit thresholds for stimulation, 4) summate, 5) accommodate, 6) show all-or-none response, and 7) have a refractory period.

8. Neurons are classified on the basis of structure (multipolar, bipolar, and unipolar) and function (sensory, motor, and association or integrative).

9. Regeneration of neurons may occur if the cell body is not damaged.

10. Only axons with a *neurilemma* are capable of regeneration.

11. Impulse initiation and conduction are dependent on an adequate stimulus and exchange of electrolytes on either side of the neuron's membrane.

12. If a threshold stimulus is applied to a neuron, the impulse is transmitted along the entire length of the neuron at a constant speed, unchanged and maximum strength. This is the basis for the all-or-none principle for neurons.

13. Impulse transmission from node to node of a peripheral neuron is called *saltatory transmission* and results in a greater speed of transmission.

14. The larger the diameter of a nerve fiber, the faster the impulse is conveyed.

15. A synapse is a functional junction between two neurons. It chemically transmits and exhibits properties such as a) one-way conduction, b) facilitation, c) inhibition, d) fatigue, e) summation, and f) is sensitive to drugs, pH, and hypoxia.

16. Conduction across synapses involves divergence and convergence.

17. Impulse conduction across a synapse, neuromuscular junction, or neuroglandular junction depends on the presence of neurotransmitter substances stored in presynaptic vesicles.

18. An excitatory impulse transmission is produced by an excitatory neuron.

19. An inhibitory impulse is produced by an inhibitory neuron to reduce or eliminate an impulse.

20. When an impulse is conducted across a synapse, synaptic vesicles release a neurotransmitter such as acetylcholine, an excitatory transmitter, which starts an impulse on the postsynaptic neuron.

21. The activity of a neurotransmitter such as acetylcholine is inhibited by the enzyme cholinesterase.

22. Other neurotransmitters are either catabolized by an enzyme or removed from the synapse through re-uptake back into the pre-synaptic structure to be reused for the next impulse.

23. Important excitatory transmitter substances include a)acetylcholine (ACh), which is inactivated by (AChE); b)norepinephrine (NE), which is inactivated by catechol-O-methyltransferase (COMT) and monoamine oxidase (MAO); c)other excitatory transmitters include serotonin, dopamine, histamine and glutamate.

24. Important inhibitory transmitter substances include gamma aminobutyric acid (GABA) and glycine.

25. Impulse transmission and conduction may be inhibited or blocked by certain drugs, and physical pressure, while stimulants like caffeine, amphetamine and benzedrine facilitate and increase synaptic transmission.

26. Neuronal regions in the brain containing thousands or even millions of neurons are arranged in patterns called circuits or conductive pathways.

27. Reflex arcs are functional units of the spinal cord and are the simplest units that can detect changes and initiate responses. Five parts are always present, and the act itself is involuntary, stereotyped, predictable and purposeful.

Summary Outline
Nervous System
Organization

I. <u>Central Nervous System</u> (CNS)-nervous tissue found making up the **Brain** & **Spinal Cord**
II. <u>Peripheral Nervous System</u> - nervous tissue coming off of the CNS - Nerves
    A. <u>Somatic Nervous System</u> - Sending and receiving information to/from voluntary muscle
    B. <u>Autonomic Nervous System</u> - Sending and receiving information to/from involuntary muscle & glands

I. General Functions:
    A. <u>sensory functions</u>: sensory receptors continuously monitoring internal & external environment, and relaying this information to CNS for interpretation.
    B. <u>integrative</u>: bringing sensory information together for perception of sensations
    B. <u>motor functions</u>: consciously and subconsciously sending impulses to effectors (muscle cells or glands).

II. Nerve tissue is made up of two types of cells.
    A. **neurons**- the structural and functional units of the nervous system.
    - react to changes in the environment or changes within the body.
    - conduct impulses to other neurons and to other cells outside the CNS.
    neuron structure:
    1. cell body - contains most of the organelles of other cells.
    2. neurofibrils - fine threads which extend into the nerve fibers supporting them.
    3. Nissl bodies(RER) are also seen here.
    4. dendrites- a fiber of a neuron which carries impulses toward the cell body. A neuron may have numerous dendrites which receives input from many other neurons.
    5. axon - a single process of a neuron which carries nerve impulses (action potentials) away from the cell body. The axon can branch at its terminal end and contact numerous other cells.
    B. **neuroglial cells**- give structural support to CNS, produce myelin, and carry on phagocytosis.
      1. *Schwann cells*-cells which commonly surround large axons in the peripheral nervous system.
        a. In large axons the membrane is composed of a lipid-protein called *myelin* which acts as an insulator and also increase the speed of a nerve impulse.
        b. Smaller axons are enclosed in Schwann cells but they are not wrapped in multiple layers and are therefore unmyelinated.
        c. Gaps between adjacent Schwann cells are called *nodes of Ranvier*.
        d. are not found in the CNS
      2. *astrocytes*- give structural support and remove cellular debris. Responsible for formation of scar tissue after CNS injuries.
      3. *oligodendrocytes*-formation of myelin within the CNS.
      4. *microglia*-phagocytosis of bacterial cells and cellular debris.
      5. *ependymal*-lines the ventricles of the brain.

III. Neuron Classification
    A. Classified according to Structure
        1. Bipolar Neurons
        2. Unipolar Neurons
        3. Multipolar Neurons
    B. Classified according to Function
        1. Sensory Neurons
        2. Interneurons
        3. Motor Neurons

IV. Cell Membrane Potential
At rest a neuron has an unequal distribution of ions on either side of the cell membrane. This causes the membrane to be electrically charged, or *polarized*.

The unequal distribution of ions inside and outside the cell membrane is determined by the presence of specific ion channels and carrier molecules.

In a resting state:
    *sodium is in a higher concentration outside the cell compared to the inside
    *potassium is in a higher concentration *inside* the cell compared to outside.

The measured potential difference in electrical charge across the membrane is called the *resting membrane potential*.

Establishing and Maintaining Resting Membrane Potential
    1. There is an unequal permeability of the membrane for sodium and potassium
        a. the membrane is more permeable (more channels) for potassium than sodium
        b. so more cations (potassium) diffuse out of the cell than cations (sodium)entering
    2. The pumping ratio of sodium to potassium ions by active transport
        a. three sodium ions pumped out for every two potassium ions pumped in (3:2 ratio)
            Three cations pumped out for every two pumped in
    3. At rest the potential difference between the inside and the outside of the cell membrane is -70mv. (negative refers to the inside being negatively charged with respect to the outside.)

Only muscle cells and neurons have the ability to manipulate (change) this difference in charge across the membrane(membrane potential). This manipulation of charge is known as a nerve impulse. To better understand impulses we need to first look at how these cells respond to an external signal.
    1. Both neurons and muscle cells exhibit the characteristic *excitability* (irritability).
    2. This means they can respond to changes in their surroundings. These changes are called *stimuli*.
    3. Stimuli cause a change in the resting potential in a particular local region of the cell membrane.
    If, in response to a stimulus the resting membrane potential becomes:
        a. more negative membrane(> -70mv, for example -76mv), the membrane is *hyperpolarizing*.
        b. less negative membrane (< -70mv, for example -57mv), the membrane is *depolarizing*

The amount of change in the membrane potential is *graded,* which means it is directly related to the strength of stimulus. A threshold stimulus is the minimal strength stimulus needed for the generation of a nerve impulse (action potentials).

Threshold is reached when a stimulus causes a depolarization of the membrane(decrease in membrane potential) to -55mv.

Threshold stimuli lead to the generation of an *action potential*.
   Events of an action potential:
   1. Gated Na+ channels open in the membrane at the point of stimulation
   2. Na^+ diffuses into the cell
   3. Membrane potential decreases *(depolarization)* to +30mv (the outside of the membrane becomes negatively charged with respect to the inside)
4. Gated K+ channels open and K^+ diffuses out of the membrane
5. Membrane potential increases *(repolarizes)* to -70mv
6. After repolarization the *Na/K pump* moves Na+ back out of the membrane and moves K+ back in to return the membrane to its original resting potential.

V. Nerve impulse-the propagation of action potentials along a nerve fiber traveling to the end of the fiber.
   1. Unmyelinated nerve fibers conduct impulses over their entire surface.
   2. In myelinated fibers the action potential jumps between nodes of Ranvier, which greatly accelerates the rate at which these impulses move along the fiber.
   All or none response- if a threshold or greater stimulus is applied the nerve impulse fires completely. This means with the formation of the first action potential, the propagation of action potentials will continue down the entire neuron membrane. The action potentials will not stop say halfway down.

VI. Synapses-the junction between two neurons.
   A. Characteristics:
      1. synaptic cleft-the space between two neurons.
      2. presynaptic neuron
      3. postsynaptic neuron
      4. synaptic vesicles
   B. Synaptic transmission-
      1. Impulses move through dendrites toward the cell body.
      2. Impulses move along an axon toward the end (synapse)
      3. When the impulse reaches the end (terminal knob) of the axon the following events occur:
         a. impulse causes calcium to move inward and fuse to vesicles containing neurotransmitters.
         b. vesicles fuse to postsynaptic membrane and release neurotransmitters into synaptic cleft.
         c. neurotransmitters attach to receptors on the postsynaptic membrane.
         d. if a threshold level is reached then an impulse is generated in the post-synaptic neuron.

VII. Neurotransmitters-substances released at synapses. Most neurons release only one type. Stored in synaptic vesicles. 35 different neurotransmitters types exist
   1- Types:
      a. Acetylcholine - ACh
      b. Monoamines- ex. epinephrine, norepinephrine, dopamine, serotonin

c. Amino Acids - glycine, glutamic acid, aspartic acid, GABA

d. Peptides - enkephalins, substance P

Note: most neurotransmitters have specific enzymes that destroy them once they are released into the synaptic cleft.

Examples: Acetylcholinesterase - breaks down Acetylcholine

Monoamine oxidases - breaks down the Monoamines

2- Neurotransmitters binding to receptors on the post synaptic neuron cause a change in the membrane potential at that local site. These changes are referred to as *synaptic potentials.* Synaptic potentials are graded. The direction in which the potential goes (depolarization or repolarization) depends on the type of neurotransmitter binding.

3- Neurotransmitters can be excitatory or inhibitory.

a- Excitatory Neurotransmitters cause decrease in membrane potential (depolarization) of the post-synaptic membrane. Excitatory Postsynaptic Potential (EPSP)

b- Inhibitory Neurotransmitters cause an increase in membrane potential (hyperpolarization) of the post synaptic membrane. Inhibitory Postsynaptic Potential (IPSP)

The sum of the EPSP's and IPSP's determines whether an action potential is generated. Remember, in order to generate an action potential, threshold must be reached.

VIII. Meninges-protective membranes which protect the CNS.

A. three layers

1. dura mater-outermost tough layer. Is attached to the skull and vertebrae.

parts of dura mater in and around the brain:

i. falx cerebri-dura between cerebral hemispheres.

ii. falx cerebelli-dura between cerebellar hemispheres.

iii. tentorium cerebelli-dura between the cerebrum and cerebellum.

Note: a blow to the head can result in damage to the blood vessels which supply the meninges. If bleeding is between the dura and the skull it is called an epidural hematoma. Bleeding between the arachnoid and dura is a subdural hematoma.

2. arachnoid-middle layer. Separated from dura by thin layer of fluid.

3. pia mater-covers surface of brain and spinal cord.

B. subarachnoid space contains cerebrospinal fluid and is the space between the arachnoid and pia mater. CSF acts as a shock absorber for the CNS.

IX. Spinal cord-continuation of brainstem which is contained in the vertebral foramen.

A. Structure:

1. composed of central core of gray matter surrounded by tracts of white matter.

2. *ventral(anterior) horn*-contains motor neurons which stimulate skeletal muscles to contract.

Figure 11 Spinal cord-structures/functions

structure	function
spinal nerve	carries impulses into/out of spinal cord
dorsal root	carries sensory information into spinal c.
dorsal root ganglion	contains cell bodies of sensory neurons
ventral(anterior)horn	contains cell bodies of motor neurons
ventral root	carries impulses to skeletal muscles
white matter	bundles of axons which carry impulses to and from the brain
gray matter	collections of nerve cell bodies

B. Functions:
    1. carry *sensory* information to brain from body(ascending tracts).
    2. carry *motor* information to muscles and glands from brain.(descending tracts).
    3. spinal reflexes.

Figure 12 Nervous system organization, flow chart

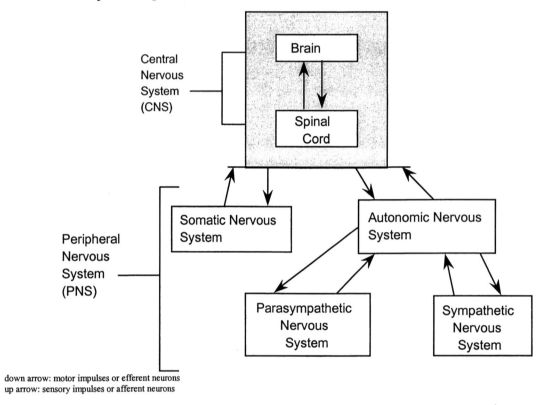

down arrow: motor impulses or efferent neurons
up arrow: sensory impulses or afferent neurons

Lecture supplement

COCAINE

How it affects the Brain

Cocaine, especially the "crack" version, rushes to the limbic system of the brain where it alters the synapses that use dopamine as its neurotransmitter. The drug will interfere with the reuptake of the neurohormone into the presynaptic end button. From this all of the individual's problems will occur.

Normal cell activity

In a normal limbic neuron the impulse releases dopamine. These dopamine synapses (excitatory type) carry impulses about pleasure, alertness and motor functions to and from the limbic system. These synapses rely on the reuptake and thus reuse of the dopamine for all subsequent or following impulses through the region. Interruption of this reuptake will alter the post synaptic activity.

How *Cocaine* blocks and alters the synapse

When the cocaine is released from blood into the synapse it blocks the reuptake of dopamine into the presynaptic neuron. The synaptic cleft begins to fill with dopamine that should have been removed as the cocaine attaches to the presynaptic membrane. This blocks the reuptake of dopamine thus causing the original dopamine to go back and contact the postsynaptic membrane again.

This recontact by the same dopamine molecules causes the postsynaptic structure to become overexcited as compared to normal activity. This heightens and continues the pleasure feeling that these synapses normally produce. Gradually the trapped dopamine is broken down by catabolic enzymes that normally are ineffective because dopamine reuptake normally would have occurred by now.

In a few weeks (and generally after only one use or "line") the presynaptic cell's stored supply of dopamine run's low. The synapse now can not function normally with this below normal level of dopamine stored in the presynaptic structure. The only way these synapses are now able to experience normal pleasure caused by these synapses is by taking _more_ of the cocaine drug and more of it than he/she did the first time. The second use will not produce the "rush" the first line did and thus the "coke" user will always be "chasing the first high".

This change in the availability of dopamine at the synapse will cause erratic changes in the membrane activity during the hours of non-drug use. Thus, behavior changes start to occur such as muscle weakness, paranoia and the first stages of depression. Because of these activities and others to come the person is now hooked.

Summary Outline

I. ANATOMICAL DIVISIONS OF THE NERVOUS SYSTEM
  A. Central Nervous System (CNS)
   1. Brain
   2. Spinal cord
  B. Peripheral Nervous System (PNS)
   1. Cranial nerves 12 pairs
   2. Spinal nerves 31 pairs
    a. Somatic nervous system: somatic afferents and somatic efferents
    b. Autonomic nervous system (ANS): visceral afferents and visceral efferents
     i. Sympathetic division (thoracolumbar)
     ii. Parasympathetic division (craniosacral)

II. FUNCTIONAL DIVISIONS OF THE NERVOUS SYSTEM
  A. Sensory division
   1. somatic afferent
   2. visceral afferent (autonomic afferent)
   3. special senses: vision, hearing, smell, taste
  B. Motor division
   1. somatic efferent
   2. visceral efferent (autonomic motor)
  C. Integrative system: interneurons (internuncials) in spine and associative centers within the brain
   1. Interpretation of sensory stimuli and responding to this input
   2. Processing and storing information within the central nervous system
   3. recalling sensory stimuli
   4. thought, creativity, emotions, etc. are the highest levels of brain activity

III. CELLULAR COMPONENTS OF THE NERVOUS SYSTEM
A. THE NEURON
  Unit of structure and function of the nervous systems
  Capable of receiving and transmitting information
  Neuron has a cell body (perikaryon, or soma); projecting from cell body one long process, the axon , and usually many short processes, the dendrites
 1. Types of neurons
   a. Unipolar
   b. Bipolar
   c. Multipolar

2. Location of Neuron cell bodies
   a. Brain and spinal cord
   b. In central nervous system
   c. Groups of cell bodies with specific function called nuclei groups of cell bodies located outside the central nervous system called ganglia, e.g., dorsal root ganglia, ganglia of the autonomic nervous system
3. Location of Neurons and Neural cell structure
   a. Single nerve fiber consists of axon surrounded by sheaths: myelin sheath and neurilemma (sheath of Schwann)
   b. In peripheral nerves Schwann cell responsible for sheaths
   c. Node of Ranvier-point where two successive Schwann cells abut on nerve fiber
   d. Nerve fibers are described as:
      i. Myelinated-these have extensive layer of myelin
      ii. Unmyelinated-these fibers have no myelin or one that is sparse
   e. Extent and thickness of myelin sheath and function of nerve fiber are the basis of classification of A, B, and C types of nerve fibers
   f. Many nerve fibers grouped together as fascicles and held together by connective tissue to form nerve trunks
      i. Perineurium-connective tissue encasing individual fascicles
      ii. Endoneurium-connective tissue around individual nerve fiber

B. NEUROGLIA
1. Neuroglia represent supportive cells of the nervous system; these cells do not possess the property of transmission of impulses
2. Ependymal cells-line ventricles of brain and central canal of spinal cord
3. Satellite cells-surround cell bodies in ganglia
4. Schwann cells-surround peripheral nerves, responsible for myelin sheath
5. Neuroglial cells of the central nervous system include:
6. Astrocytes-found in association with blood vessels and neurons
7. Oligodendrocytes-cells responsible for forming myelin in nerve fibers of the central nervous system
8. Microglia-macrophages of the central nervous system

IV. FUNCTIONAL CLASSIFICATION OF NERVES
Somatic nerves-convey information to voluntary structures, e.g., skeletal muscles
Visceral nerves-convey information to involuntary structures, e.g., smooth and cardiac muscle and glands
Sensory or afferent nerves - from a sensory receptor to the central nervous system
Motor or efferent-from central nervous system to an effector organ

A. SENSORY RECEPTORS
1. Classification by location
   a. Exteroceptors-receive stimuli from the body surface
   b. Interoceptors-receive stimuli from internal organs
   c. Proprioceptors-receive stimuli from muscles, tendons, and joints

2. Classification by function
   a. Mechanoreceptors
      i. Pressure, touch: free endings, pacinian and Meissner's corpuscles
      ii. Kinesthesia: free endings and pacinian corpuscles on tendons, joints
      iii. Hearing: receptors in inner ear
      iv. Equilibrium: vestibular apparatus in inner ear
      v. Muscle and tendon stretch: muscle spindles, Golgi tendon apparatus
   b. Thermoreceptors: free nerve endings, Ruffini, Krause endings
   c. Chemoreceptors: taste buds, olfactory cells, receptors of carotid and aortic bodies
   d. Photosensitive receptors: retina of eye
   e. Baroreceptors: in aortic arch and carotid sinus

B. SPECIFICITY OF RECEPTORS
Receptor Stimuli
1. Stimuli are physical or chemical changes in the immediate environment
2. Changes in environment are converted into a rhythmical succession of nervous impulses
3. Adequate stimulus, the kind of physical or chemical change to which the receptor is sensitive
4. Minimal stimulus, the least change that can excite a receptor
5. Subliminal stimulus, a stimulus below the threshold level that fails to excite
6. Intensity of stimulus, probably related to the degree of change at the receptor and reflected in the frequency of impulses initiated

C. ADAPTATION

Adaptation of end organs varies in relation to the speed with which they reach approximate equilibrium with their environment

1. Slow adaptation, long trains (sequences) of nerve impulses issue from end organs in response to prolonged stimulation
2. Rapid adaptation, short trains of impulses issue from end organs even though stimulus is prolonged

V. NEURAL MEMBRANE ACTIVITY

A. RESTING MEMBRANE (GRADED POTENTIAL)

1. Because of diffusion and active transport, concentration and type of ions are different on inside and outside of membrane
2. In resting state more positively charged ions on outside of membrane and more negatively charged ions on inside (a polarized membrane)

B. ACTIVE STATE: IMPULSE OR ACTION POTENTIAL

1. Stimulus causes a sudden increase in permeability of nerve membrane to sodium ions, which causes rapid changes in membrane potential; sequence of changes that occur termed action potential
2. Sequence of Events
   a. Initial entry of Na^+ ions cancels polarity of membrane-depolarization
   b. Na+ ions inside of nerve membrane change polarity; inside becomes positive, outside negative
   c. Return of membrane to resting state-repolarization
   d. Action potential is propagated along entire length of nerve in nerve fibers that are unmyelinated
   e. Conduction of impulse down neuron or nerve
   f. In myelinated fibers impulses are conducted from one node of Ranvier to next; process referred to as saltatory transmission
3. Excitability Periods
   Excitability of nerve fiber shows three periods:
   a. Normal period or phase
   b. Absolute refractory period, a short period during which the nerve fiber is unexcitable to any stimulus regardless of strength
   c. Relative refractory period, period of less excitability than normal phase-stronger-than-normal stimulus required to excite

VI. SYNAPSE

A. Basics
1. One of the functional units within the nervous system
2. The functional connection between two neurons
3. Point of continuity that permits transmission of activity from one neuron to another
4. Normal pH from 7.35 to 7.45
   a. Alkalosis (an increase in pH) above 7.45 up to 8.0 results in increased excitability of neurons that can cause cerebral convulsions
   b. Acidosis (decrease in pH) below 7.35 down to 6.80 results in a depression of neuron activity and can produce a comatose state (coma).
B. Modified types
1. Neuroglandular junction - a neuron and gland
2. Neuromuscular junction - neuron and muscle (part of a motor unit)
C. Types based on anatomy
   axosomatic, axodendritic, axoaxonic, dendrodendritic
D. Two types functionally: excitatory and inhibitory
E. Two types based on mode of action
1. Chemical - a neurohormone or neurotransmitter substance is required to alter the postsynaptic membrane
   a. Excitatory - promotes an impulse through the synapse
   b. Inhibitory - alters, partially blocks or completely blocks the movement of an impulse through the synapse
   Both of these can fatigue because of overuse and/or depletion neurohormone
2. Electrical - no neurohormone but rather an action potential of the presynaptic causes the post synaptic membrane to depolarize thus generating an action potential. Does not fatigue. Ex. retina of eye and between cardiac muscle fibers at the intercalated discs

F. Properties of the Synapse
   1. Transmission of activity from one neuron to another involves a chemical neurotransmitter
      a. Conduction at synapse slower than along nerve fiber; reflects time for diffusion of transmitter across synaptic cleft
      b. Excitatory and inhibitory types of synapses
      c. Fatigue occurs more readily at synapses; more easily affected by drugs
      d. Transmission in one direction only
      e. The point of origin for >95 % of all impulses
G. Distribution of neurotransmitters
   1. Somatic nervous system (efferent division) at neuromuscular junction - acetylcholine - ACh (nicotinic)
   2. Autonomic nervous system
      a. Preganglionic (sympathetic & parasympathetic) ACh (nicotinic)
      b. Parasympathetic postganglionic - ACh (muscarinic)
      c. Sympathetic postganglionic - most release norepinephrine at a (alpha) and b (beta) receptors few are cholinergic(they release acetylcholine)
   3. Central nervous system
      a. Spinal cord: ACh and glycine
      b. lower brain: epinephrine, norepinephrine, dopamine, serotonin, GABA
      c. higher brain: ACh, cyclic AMP, prostaglandins, norepinephrine
H. Cholinergic Mechanisms
   1. Cholinergic receptors
      a. *nicotinic* - curare blocks
      Locations - somatic efferents, autonomic preganglionic, CNS neurons
      b. *muscarinic* - atropine blocks
      Locations - parasympathetic post ganglionic, CNS neurons
   2. Adrenergic Mechanisms
      a. Catecholamines
         i. norepinephrine - most post ganglionic sympathetic and certain CNS neurons
         ii. dopamine - CNS neurons (extrapyramidal system) and interneurons, autonomic ganglia
         iii. epinephrine - most originate from the adrenal medulla NOT the sympathetic nervous system
I. Methods of removal from synaptic cleft
   1. reuptake or neurohormone into presynaptic structure by active transport
   2. enzymolysis by MAO (monoamine oxidase) or COMT (catechol-O-methyltransferase)
J. Three functional types of adrenergic receptors
   1. peripheral α (alpha) excitatory receptors
   2. peripheral β (beta) inhibitory receptors (β_2)
   3. cardiac β excitatory receptors (β_1)

VII. Neural Connections (circuits) and pathways - groups of neurons functionally connected
A. instinct - (innate, performed or genetic)
   1. simple instinct responses (reflexes):
   spinal cord reflexes, breathing, heart rate, basal metabolism, pupil dilation
   2. complex instinct behavior (patterned behavioral responses)
   feeding, sexual behaviors, survival responses, aggression, etc.
      a. acquired circuits (learned)
         piano playing, sports, driving a car, etc.
      b. overall behavior (personality)
         complex composition and interaction of instincts and acquired behaviors

---

PRACTICE TEST QUESTIONS-

1. All neurons function in:
   a. receiving impulses
   b. sending impulses
   c. forming and conducting impulses
   d. reflex arcs

2. The ions most directly involved in establishing an excitable state or resting potential are:
   a. sodium and potassium
   b. calcium and potassium
   c. chloride and potassium
   d. chloride and sodium

3. The first structure of a neuron that controls the impulse is the:
   a. axon

b. synapse
c. dendrite
d. cell body

4. The central nervous system is composed of the:
   a. spinal cord and spinal nerves
   b. brain and spinal nerves
   c. brain and cranial nerves
   d. brain and spinal cord

True and False

1. _____ The conductible units of the nervous system are the neurons.
2. _____ Nissl bodies synthesize proteins for the neuron.
3. _____ Ependymal synthesize myelin in the CNS.
4. _____ Dendrites conduct impulses toward the cell body.
5. _____ A synapse controls the direction of nerve impulse through a neural pathway.
6. _____ A resting nerve membrane is charged due to K^+ movement.
7. _____ A neuron without a functional nucleus cannot conduct an impulse.
8. _____ Glial cells only connect to and support neurons.
9. _____ The refractory period controls the number of impulses a neuron can transmit per second.
10. _____ Acetylcholine is the only excitatory synaptic transmitter used in the nervous system.

Matching

_____ Neuron
_____ Glia
_____ Nerve Impulse
_____ Synapse
_____ Myelin sheath
_____ Axon
_____ Neurilemma
_____ Astrocytes
_____ Facilitation
_____ Wallerian degeneration
_____ Acetylcholine
_____ Forebrain
_____ Midbrain
_____ Hindbrain
_____ Parasympathetic system
_____ Sympathetic system
_____ Sensory neuron
_____ Motor neuron

a. Junction between neurons
b. Increasing ease of synaptic functions
c. Contains cerebrum
d. Product of Schwann cell; its membrane
e. A nerve cell
f. Conserves body resources and energy
g. Degenerative changes in a peripheral nerve fiber
h. Carries impulses toward CNS
i. Depolarization moving across a cell memebrane
j. Between forebrain and hindbrain
k. Glial cell forming supporting networks in CNS
l. Carries impulses to muscle and glands
m. Connecting, and supporting cells for neurons
n. Forms cerebellum and medulla of adult
o. Efferent process of a neuron
q. A synaptic transmitter
r. Segmented fatty sheath on a nerve fiber
s. Speeds activity of most body systems

ANSWERS

Multiple Choice
1. c 2. a 3. b 4. d

True and False
1. True 2. True 3. False 4. True 5. True 6. False 7. True 8. False 9. True 10. False

Matching
E,M,I,A,R,E,D,K,B,G,Q,C,J,N,F,S,H,L

Spinal cord, Spinal nerves and Spinal Reflexes

Overview

This unit first considers the structural groupings of neural tissue and then principal anatomical and functional characteristics of the spinal cord. Also discussed are spinal puncture and the factors responsible for maintaining and protecting the spinal cord. The importance of reflexes are categorized according to type, and several clinically important reflexes are described. In addition, spinal nerves, plexuses, and dermatomes are considered.

Chapter Objectives

1. Discuss the structure and functions of the spinal cord.
2. Describe the three menix layers that surround the central nervous system.
3. Explain the roles of white matter and gray matter in processing and relaying sensory information and motor commands.
4. Describe the gross anatomical components and their interrelationships within the nervous system.
5. Describe the structure, function and interaction of components within the spinal cord and spinal nerves.
6. Demonstrate an ability to relate anatomical structures of the peripheral nervous system with noticeable surface anatomy landmarks.
7. Describe the structure and function of the meninges and circulatory system.
8. Describe the major components of a spinal nerve.
9. Relate the distribution pattern of spinal nerves to the regions they innervate.
10. Describe the process of a neural reflex.
11. Classify the types of reflexes, and explain the functions of each.
12. Distinguish between the types of motor responses produced by various reflexes.
13. Explain how reflexes interact to produce complex behaviors.
14. Explain how higher centers control and modify reflex responses.

Concepts and Definitions

1.   Neural tissue is grouped into highly organized structural and functional masses. Examples include white matter, gray matter, nerves, ganglia, tracts, nuclei, and horns.
2.   The spinal cord is a cylindrical structure with two conspicuous dorsal enlargements. It is a series of 31 segments, each segment giving rise to a pair of spinal nerves.
3.   The spinal cord is protected by the meninges, the cerebrospinal fluid, vertebral ligaments and within the vertebral canal of the vertebra.
4.   The spinal cord serves as a two-way conduction pathway between the brain and periphery.
5.   The white matter of the spinal cord is arranged into tracts that convey sensory impulses to the brain (afferent) and motor impulses (efferent) to skeletal muscles.
6.   Cerebrospinal fluid circulates throughout the central nervous system. Removal of the fluid is by spinal (lumbar) puncture.

7. The functional unit of the spinal cord is the reflex arc. All reflex arcs contain a receptor, sensory neuron, inter neuron, motor neuron, and effector.
8. A reflex is a quick, unconscious involuntary response to a stimulus transmitted over a reflex arc.
9. The reflex is the major mechanism of the nervous system for an immediate response to changes in the environment.
10. Reflexes are important in diagnosing disorders of the nervous system and for locating the site of injury through the testing of myotatic (muscle response) reflexes.
11. Spinal nerves are called mixed nerves because the posterior root contains sensory fibers and the anterior root contains motor fibers.
12. The 31 pairs of spinal nerves are named and numbered according to the region and level of the spinal cord from which they emerge.
13. Most spinal nerves form networks called plexuses.
14. The skin segment supplied by a spinal nerve is a dermatome.
15. A variety of spinal tracts carry impulses to and from the brain and into various levels within the cord.
16. Spinal shock occurs when the cord is traumatized.
17. Spinal cord injury could result from transection, which is a partial or complete severing of the spinal cord.
18. Axons that have a neurilemma can be repaired if the cell body is intact and fibers are in close association with Schwann cells.
19. **NEURITIS** is inflammation of a single nerve, two or more nerves in separate areas, or many nerves simultaneously. **SCIATICA** is a type of neuritis characterized by severe pain along the path of the Sciatic nerve or its branches.
20. **SHINGLES** is an acute viral infection of spinal nerves that damages and inflames the skin at the end of the nerves. It is caused by the _Herpes zoster_ virus. One treatment consists of injecting a local anesthetic into nerve junctions to relieve pain, weaken the virus and accelerate healing.

Summary Outline

I. SPINAL CORD

A. Spinal Cord Location and Shape:
1. Located inside vertebral column.
2. Average length, 45 cm.
3. Originates at level of foramen magnum and extends downward to end between first and second lumbar vertebrae.
4. Cylindrical in shape; two enlargements, one at the cervical region and another at the lumbar region.
5. Tapers at it's inferior end into conus medullaris, from which projects one filum terminale.

B. Spinal Cord Protected By:
1. Membranes/meninges:
   a). Dura mater = outer membrane.
   b). Arachnoid mater = middle membrane.
   c). Pia mater = innermost membrane.
2. Bony vertebral column
3. Fluid medium: Cerebrospinal fluid.

C. Appearance in Transverse Section:
1. Central region of gray matter in shape of letter H surround by white matter.
2. In center of gray matter is central canal.
3. Region of gray matter around central canal is _gray commisure_.

4. Gray matter divided into columns or horns:
   a). Posterior
   b). Anterior
   c).Intermedialateral
5. White matter divided into funiculi:
   a). Posterior
   b). Anterior
   c). Lateral

II. SPINAL CORD TRACTS

A. Short Tracts (also called: intersegmental fasciculi, association tracts, ground bundles)
B. Long Tracts (projection tracts)
   1. Ascending tracts (sensory tracts)
      a. Contains first order neuron, second order neuron and third order neuron to form the pathway that contains the following sensory tracts
      b. Conscious sensation or recognition (reaches thalamus)
      c. Sensory Anterior tracts
         i. Spinothalamic tract
         ii. Lateral and anterior pathways
         iii. Pathways for pain, crude thermal sensations, tickle, itch, tactile, pressure and sexual stimulation generated by touch
      d. Dorsal column systems
         2 tracts: fasciculus gracilis and fasciculus cuneatus
      e. functions:
         i. Unconscious sensation or recognition (does not reach thalamus)
         ii. Spinotectal tract - spinovisual reflexes
         iii. Spinolivary tract - proprioceptive sensation to cerebellum
         iv. Spinocerebellar tract - conveys proprioceptive information from skeletal muscles, tendons and joints to the cerebellum causing an adjustment of skeletal muscle tone and synergistic activity.
   2. Descending tracts (motor control)
      a. Formed by two motor neurons
         i. - Upper motor neurons (starts in brain)
         ii. - Lower motor neurons (starts in anterior horn gray of spinal cord)
      b. Pyramidal tract system (voluntary and discrete skeletal muscle movements)
         i. Corticospinal tract (cerebrospinal) -
         ii. Neuron cell bodies originate in cerebral cortex (30% from motor area, 20% from premotor area and 25 % from sensory cortex)
         iii. Corticobulbar tract -
            a. Descends with corticospinal fibers and distribute to motor nuclei of the cranial nerves in the brain stem
            b. Provides voluntary efferents to head muscles
            c. Extrapyramidal tract system (responsible for postural, gross and fixation movements)
               i. Vestibulospinal tract - transmits cerebellar information into spine and conveys the efferent component of the efferent system
               ii. Tectospinal tract - fibers originate in tectum and end in ventral horn of spinal cord. Form efferent component of spinotectal reflexes
               iii. Rubrospinal tract - fibers arise in red nucleus of brain and descend into spine. Convey subconscious stereotypic motor activities from midbrain.

iv. Reticulospinal tract - Arise from cells scattered throughout the reticular formation of brain and brainstem and terminate in ventral and lateral horns of cord. Conveys muscle tone output to ventral horn lower motor neurons. Can also carry impulses for the sympathetic and parasympathetic nervous systems.

III. UPPER AND LOWER MOTOR NEURONS

A. UPPER MOTOR NEURON

1. These include all of the descending fiber systems that can influence and modify the activity of the lower motor neuron
2. These descending neural impulses from the upper motor neurons which are transmitted to spinal levels by a group of heterogeneous tracts are concerned with the following functions:
   a. mediation of somatic motor activity
   b. control of skeletal muscle tone
   c. maintenance of posture and equilibrium
   d. mediation of reflex activity
   e. modification or control of sensory stimuli
   f. innervation of viscera and autonomic structures
3. Lesions (damage) will usually be located at three levels in the CNS:
   a. The brain stem
   b. The cerebral cortex
   c. The spinal cord
      i. Causes of Lesions: vascular disease, trauma, neoplasm, infections, degeneration
      ii. Characteristic Symptoms of Upper Motor neuron lesions
         a. paresis (weakening of the muscles)
         b hypertonicity and spasticity (resistance to passive movements)
         c. hyperreflexia (overreaction to a stimulus) or spasticity
         d. abnormal or unexpected reflexes (i.e. Babinski sign: stroke plantar surface and the response is the fanning of toes)
4. Lesions of the Cerebral Cortex and Brainstem
   a. Unilateral lesions will produce contralateral paralysis usually hemiplegia (paralysis to one side)
   b. The most common in the brain is the CVA (cerebrovascular accident) or stroke.
5. Lesions of the Spinal Cord
   a. The lower and upper motor neurons are important clinically. If the lower motor neuron is damaged or diseased, there is neither voluntary nor reflex action of the muscle it innervates. The muscle remains in a relaxed non-contracted state called **flaccid paralysis** . Injury or disease of the upper motor neurons in a motor pathway is characterized by varying degrees of continued muscle contraction. This produces exaggerated reflexes and is called **spasticity** . This upper motor neuron damage is demonstrated in the Babinski sign. This is dorsiflexion of the great toe accompanied by fanning of the lateral toes in response to stroking the plantar surface along the outer border of the foot. This response is normal only in infants with undeveloped reflex activity and reflex arc. Normal adult response should be to plantar flex the toes.
   b. Lesions of the descending tracts, most common the result of trauma are usually bilateral and produce **paraplegia** (paralysis of legs and lower part of the body for both motor and sensory loss).
6. Neurological Disorders Affecting Upper Motor Neurons
   a. Neurosyphilis
   b. Cerebral Palsy
   c. Parkinson's disease
   d. Treatment: L-DOPA and surgical destruction of partial thalamus to reduce rigidity and tremor but not aninesia (absence of movement) or the dysarthria (stuttering of speech).

e. Huntington's Chorea or Huntington's disease
   Familial disease and involves a severe degeneration and atrophy of caudate nuclei and lenticular
   nuclei.
f. Multiple Sclerosis
   Progressive demyelination occurring in disseminated patches in the brain and spinal cord

B. LOWER MOTOR NEURONS
1. Two types of cells in the anterior horn
   a. Column cells - cells and processes confined to CNS (also called interneurons)
   b. Root cells - processes emerge from spinal cord and serve two effector functions
2. Lesions (damage) and characteristics of lower motor neuron damage
   a. Paresis (muscle weakness) or complete paralysis
   b. Hypotonia or atonia (loss of muscle tone) which appears as flaccidity (flaccid paralysis)
   c. Areflexia (loss of reflex activity due to in interruption of the reflex arc)
   d. Atrophy of muscle: becomes evident 2-3 weeks
   e. Lesions of lower motor neurons may occur at various levels
3. Neurological disorders affecting lower motor neurons
   a. Poliomyelitis-viral disease affecting motor neuron at various levels but primarily respiratory
   b. Amyotrophic lateral sclerosis (Lou Gherig's disease)-etiology unknown, a gradual wasting of muscles
      with no energy thus fatigue is systemic
   c. Neuritis or polyneuritis
   d. Myasthenia gravis - disease of the motor end plate characterized by muscular weakness and atrophy
      and treated with anti-AChase agents

VIII. THE REFLEX ARC
A. Definition: The structures used by a reflex.
B. The functional unit of the brain and spinal cord.
C. Represents physiologic mechanism by which organism adapts to its external and internal
   environment
D. Structures
   1. Sensory receptor
   2. Sensory (afferent) neuron
   3. One or more synapses
   4. Motor (efferent) neuron
   5. Effector organ, e.g., voluntary and involuntary muscles, glands
E. Types by Anatomy
   1. Monosynaptic reflex arc, e.g., "knee jerk"
   2. Polysynaptic reflex arc, e.g., withdrawal of limb in response to noxious stimulus
F. Types by Function
   1. Somatic reflex arc - effector organ skeletal muscle
   2. Autonomic reflex arc (visceral reflex arc) - effector organ smooth muscle, cardiac muscle, or gland
      tissue

PRACTICE TEST QUESTIONS

1. A spinal puncture places the needle tip in the:
   a. fourth ventricle
   b. subarachnoid space
   c. central canal
   d. choroid plexus

2. The adult human spinal cord does not extend beyond
   vertebra:
   a. T-5
   b. S-2
   c. C-12
   d. L-2

3. The term sulcus, used in connection with the CNS refers to:
   a. a shallow groove
   b. a deep groove
   c. an upfold
   d. the tapering tip of the cord

4. Gray matter contains:
   a. mostly blood vessels
   b. mostly myelinated nerve fibers
   c. mostly neuron cell bodies and synapses
   d. mostly cerebrospinal fluid

5. A spinal tract carrying voluntary motor impulses to skeletal muscles is the:
   a. Gracile
   b. corticospinal
   c. Rubrospinal
   d. spinocerebellar

6. A spinal tract carrying sensations of touch is the:
   a. reticulospinal
   b. spinothalamic
   c. spinocerebellar
   d. gracilus

7. The spinal cord is an important area for:
   a. reflex control of muscle
   b. sensory interpretation
   c. control of equilibrium
   d. vision

8. How many pairs of spinal nerves branch from the spinal cord?
   a. 35
   b. 30
   c. 31
   d. 26

9. The plexus from which the Sciatic nerve arises is:
   a. brachial
   b. sacral
   c. cervical
   d. lumbar

10. Damage to the upper motor neuron causes:
    a. loss of sensory function
    b. flaccid paralysis
    c. no effect
    d. spastic paralysis

11. Damage to the lower motor neuron causes:
    a. loss of sensory function
    b. flaccid paralysis
    c. no effect
    d. spastic paralysis

12. The first type of activity to reappear after spinal shock is/are:
    a. visceral reflexes
    b. flexion reflexes
    c. simple reflexes, e.g., knee jerk
    d. sexual reflexes

13. The functional unit of the nervous system that automatically controls body function is the:
    a. axon
    b. dendrite
    c. glial cell
    d. reflex arc
    e. neuron

14. Reflex arcs:
    a. contain a receptor, afferent neuron, center, efferent neuron, and effector
    b. always produce the same effect
    c. are often used to determine function of the central nervous system
    d. all of the above

| True and False |

1. _____ White matter of the cord contains ascending and descending motor and sensory pathways.

2. _____ The spinal nerves exit through vertebral foramina.

3. _____ Gray matter contains neuron cell bodies and synapses.

4. _____ Ventral gray columns contain cell bodies for voluntary muscle control.

5. _____ The adult spinal cord extends the length of the spinal cord.

6. _____ Cell bodies of sensory neurons are found within the cord.

7. _____ The spinothalamic tracts convey sensations of pain, heat, and cold.

8. _____ A spinal tap is made at the level of the 4th lumbar vertebra.

9. _____ An injection into the deltoid muscle could damage the sciatic nerve.

10. _____ There are two meninges around the cord.

Completion

1. The three meninges of the CNS, from inside outwards are the:

2. Three functions of the spinal cord include:

3. Muscle sense concerned with muscle tone and posture is carried over the _____ tracts.

4. There are _____ (how many?) cervical spinal nerves.

5. A plexus is defined as:

6. A reflex arc includes 5 structures:

7. Reflexes are:

_____ Vertebral Canal	a. The neuron from brain to cord for motor impulses
_____ Pia mater	b. Tapering tip of spinal cord
_____ Dura mater	c. Contains cell bodies of sensory neurons
_____ Conus medullaris	d. The group of spinal nerves arising from the lower cord segments
_____ Spinal tract	e. Median, musculocutaneous, radial, ulnar, axillary nerves
_____ Upper motor neuron	f. Houses the spinal cord
_____ Lower motor neuron	g. The result of hemisection of the spinal cord
_____ Myotatic reflex	h. Conveys sensory impulses to the cord
_____ Cauda equina	i. A region in the white mater of the cord carrying particular impulses
_____ Dorsal root	j. Fall of blood pressure when arising
_____ Spinal ganglion	l. Nerve of the cervical plexus to diaphragm
_____ Plexus	m. Vascular membrane of the CNS
_____ Brachial Plexus nerves	n. Temporary synaptic depression after spinal trauma
_____ Sciatic nerve	o. Major nerve of the sacral plexus
_____ Brown-Sequard syndrome	p. Motor neuron from cord to muscle
_____ Spinal shock	q. A grouping of nerve fibers in the periphery
_____ Postural hypotension	r. Supply abdominal muscles
_____ Spinal anesthesia	s. "Hard mother"; protective, tough membrane of CNS
_____ Phrenic nerve	t. Induced by spinal tap and injection of anesthetic
_____ Intercostal nerves	u. Simplest unit capable of detecting and then causing a response
_____ reflex arc	v. An interneuron or association neuron in a reflex arc
_____ interneuron	w. NONE OF THESE CHOICES

ANSWERS

Brain and Cranial nerves

Overview

This unit considers the principal anatomical and functional characteristics of the brain, its protection, covering, blood supply, and the formation and circulation of cerebrospinal fluid. Also discussed are the electroencephalogram [EEG], cranial nerves, brain lateralization, the split-brain concept and neurotransmitter substances in the brain. Among the disorders of the nervous system considered are poliomyelitis, syphilis, cerebral palsy, Parkinson's, multiple sclerosis [MS], epilepsy, cerebral vascular accidents [CVA], dyslexia, Tay-Sachs disease, headaches, and trigeminal neuralgia.

Chapter Objectives

1. Name the major regions of the brain, and describe their functions.
2. Name the ventricles of the brain, and describe their locations and the connections between them.
3. Explain how the brain is protected and supported.
4. Discuss the formation, circulation, and functions of the cerebrospinal fluid.
5. Locate the motor, sensory, and association areas of the cerebral cortex, and discuss their functions.
6. Explain how information is transmitted from the brain to a muscle.
7. Describe how information is transmitted from a neural cell body to the end organ.
8. Recognize the impact of cerebellar and basal ganglia function on human movement.
9. Identify important structures within each region of the brain, and explain their functions.
10. Identify the cranial nerves, and relate each nerve to its principal destinations and functions.
11. Describe the changes in the central nervous system across the life of an individual.

Concepts and Definitions

1. The brain consists of the cerebrum, brain stem (medulla, pons, midbrain, diencephalon), and the cerebellum.
2. The cerebrum consists of two hemispheres divided into lobes that analyze sensory input and control motor functions. Basal ganglia, the limbic system, pyramidal and extrapyramidal systems are complex and integrating structures of afferent and efferent impulses.
3. The brain stem connects with the spinal cord and contains medulla, pons, midbrain, thalamus, and hypothalamus.
4. The brain is protected by the cranial bones, meninges, and cerebrospinal fluid.
5. The brain is well supplied with blood vessels which supply oxygen, nutrients, blood glucose and collect metabolic wastes.
6. The brain receives its blood through the internal carotid arteries and vertebral arteries and join at the base of the brain to become part of the Circle of Willis.
7. Continual blood supply, with its content of blood glucose [dextrose] and oxygen, is essential to the functioning of the central nervous system.
8. The spinal cord receives blood from spinal arteries and from spinal branches from the aorta.
9. Venous drainage of the brain is provided by dural sinuses (cerebral veins), and of the cord by spinal veins.

10. Solutes are restricted in their passage from the cerebral capillaries into the CNS by a blood-brain barrier.

11. Blockage or rupture of a cerebral artery may lead to lesions, that cause cell death and loss of function (stroke). A more or less common series of symptoms will develop as neuron function is compromised or impaired

12. Cerebrospinal fluid is formed primarily by filtration from networks of capillaries called choroid plexuses within the cerebral ventricles.

13. Four ventricles (cavities) within the brain are filled with cerebrospinal fluid (CSF). Subarachnoid spaces around the brain and cord and between the meninges also contain the fluid.

14. CSF is produced by choroid plexuses in ventricles I through IV, acts as a shock absorber, metabolic collector and keeps cranial volume constant. Hydrocephalus is associated with excess CSF production, or with the failure to reabsorb it back into the circulatory system.

15. Analyses of cerebrospinal fluid are used to determine many disorders of the CNS (inflammation, rupture of blood vessels, infection, meningitis, etc.).

16. The medulla (medulla oblongata) is a conduction pathway for impulses between the brain and spinal cord and contains the vital reflex centers for cardiac control, respiratory control, blood pressure control by changing blood vessel diameter, and the non-vital functions of swallowing, sneezing, coughing and vomiting.

17. The pons (pons varolii) serves as a bridge that connects the brain with the spinal cord and other parts of the brain with each other and to the cerebellum. The pons also contains nuclei for cranial nerves.

18. The cerebellum coordinates sensory or afferent impulses from all body areas concerned with movement and muscle tone, and controls direction and when to stop motions.

19. The midbrain conveys motor and sensory impulses, coordinates visual and auditory reflexes, and contains nuclei for cranial nerves.

20. The thalamus conveys all sensory impulses excluding the sense of smell to the cerebrum, responsible for the conscious recognition of pain and also, for emotional expression. It is the center for addiction to opium, heroin and morphine.

21. The hypothalamus is the control center for the autonomic nervous system, integrates the nervous systems, serves as the center for mind-over-matter phenomena, controls body temperature, contains centers for appetite, satiety, kidney electrolyte and water balance, thirst and pituitary (hypophysis) control.

22. The three general functions of the cerebrum are motor (skeletal muscle movement), sensory (interpretation and understanding of sensory impulses), and association or integration (emotional and intellectual).

23. The reticular formation (RAS) arouses or alerts the individual and determines the level of consciousness.

24. A diagnostic record of brain waves is an electroencephalogram (EEG).

25. According to the concept of brain lateralization, specialized brain functions are not symmetrical. Each hemisphere assumes a dominant role for particular functions. This is the right brain-left brain concept.

26. The cerebellum is a motor area of the brain that coordinates unconscious movements of skeletal muscles.

27. There are at least 30 different chemicals known to be or suspected to be neuro transmitter substances in the brain. Among the excitatory transmitters are acetylcholine (ACh), norepinephrine (NE), dopamine (DA), serotonin, glutamic acid, and aspartic acid. Central nervous system inhibitory transmitters include gamma aminobutyric acid (GABA) and glycine.

28. An identified group of chemical messengers in the brain is known as peptides or modified amino acids. These include enkephalins, endorphins, and dynorphin. Enkephalins and endorphins are believed to be body's natural pain killers. Other peptides include angiotensin, cholecystokinin (CCK), neurotensin, and regulating factors.

29. Of the 12 pairs of cranial nerves, 10 pairs originate from the brain stem. The cranial nerves are named by two methods--with roman numerals and with names. Cranial nerve function is easily assessed by a variety of simple tests.

30. Computerized transaxial tomography (CT scan) is a diagnostic technique used to study the structure of the brain. It is a form of radiological imaging that provides three-dimensional views.

31. NMR (nuclear magnetic resonance) can measure the metabolic activity of brain structures.

32. Poliomyelitis is caused by a group of three viruses that destroys motor nerve cells of the anterior horns of the spinal cord.

33. In advanced syphilis, the causative bacterium may attack the meninges, brain cells, and posterior columns of the spinal cord.

34. Cerebral palsy is a group of motor disorders caused by damage to cerebral nuclei, the cerebrum, or cerebellum. The individual appears to be drunk or intoxicated.

35. Parkinson's is a disorder related to malfunction of the cerebral nuclei.

36. Multiple sclerosis is a progressive destruction of the myelin sheaths of neurons of the central nervous system. The cause appears to be a scar tissue that invades the myelin sheath of motor neurons and their pathways.

37. Epilepsy is a disorder characterized by short, recurrent periodic attacks of motor, sensory, and/or psychological malfunction. It is initiated by abnormal and irregular electrical impulses from brain neurons. The two principal types of seizures are grand mal and petit mal.

38. A cerebral vascular accident (CVA), or stroke, is destruction of brain tissue resulting from disorders of blood vessels that supply the brain.

39. Dyslexia a disease in the cerebral cortex of the occipital lobe produces difficulty in handling words and symbols.

40. Tay-Sachs disease is a central nervous system affliction that usually causes death before age five.

41. Based on origin, two general types of headache are distinguished: intracranial and extracranial.

LECTURE SUPPLEMENT
THE VENTRICULAR SYSTEM

STRUCTURE

The brain has four cavities or ventricles which contain CSF. There are two lateral ventricles in the lower medial region and separated by the septum pellucidum but connected by an opening to the inferior and medial third ventricle. The opening is the foramen of Monro or interventricular foramen. This third ventricle is connected to the most inferior 4th ventricle by the aqueduct of Sylvius or cerebral aqueduct. This last ventricle is connected into the subarachnoid space around the cerebellum through three foramina: one foramen of Magendie and two foramina of Luschka. Each ventricle has choroid plexus tissue to produce CSF.

DESCRIPTION

The CSF functions as a CNS shock absorber and collector of metabolic wastes. It fills the subarachnoid spaces of the brain and spinal cord.

Specific Gravity	1.007 (WATER = 1.000)
pH	7.35
Appearance	Clear, colorless odorless
Red blood cells	None
White blood cells	0-8/uL
Protein	4 to 45 mg/dL (varies from the cord to brain)
Glucose	45 - 75 mg/dL
Microorganisms	None
Hydrostatic Pressure	60 - 150 mm H_2O

FORMATION AND REABSORPTION OF CSF

The fluid is formed from the blood plasma through specialized blood vessels called the choroid plexuses. These vessels are found in each ventricle and constantly produce at the rate of approximately of 400 - 500 cc every 24 hours. In general this filtrate composition is approximately equal to blood except for extremely large proteins that cannot pass through the semipermeable membrane. Reabsorption is through modified capillaries called arachnoid granulations of the subarachnoid space within the major cerebral sinuses. Reabsorption equals CSF production every 24 hours.

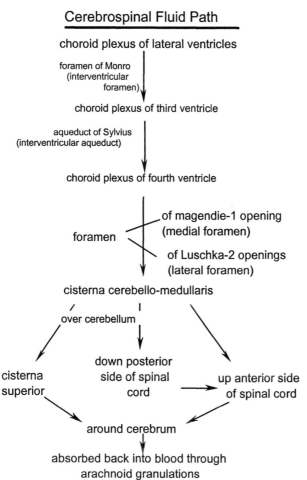

Cerebrospinal Fluid Path

choroid plexus of lateral ventricles

foramen of Monro (interventricular foramen)

choroid plexus of third ventricle

aqueduct of Sylvius (interventricular aqueduct)

choroid plexus of fourth ventricle

foramen — of magendie-1 opening (medial foramen) / of Luschka-2 openings (lateral foramen)

cisterna cerebello-medullaris

over cerebellum

down posterior side of spinal cord

cisterna superior

up anterior side of spinal cord

around cerebrum

absorbed back into blood through arachnoid granulations

Figure 13 Cerebrospinal fluid path

This fluid is slowly produced from the choroid plexuses. The fluid that originates in the right lateral ventricle (in right hemisphere) and the fluid from the left lateral ventricle (in left hemisphere) moves into the third ventricle through the interventricular foramen (foramen of Monro). The third ventricle adds more fluid and now is moved into the 4th ventricle through the aqueduct of Sylvius (interventricular aqueduct).

From the fourth ventricle the CSF exists into the subarachnoid space of the cerebellum through three foramina. From here, some of the CSF passes down over the spinal cord and returns up to the subarachnoid spaces of the cerebral hemispheres. Spinal fluid fills the tubular extension of the subarachnoid space which forms a sleeve around the spinal cord. All of the CSF will eventually return into the venous blood of the sagittal sinus through the arachnoid granulations. NOTE: Review your lecture and laboratory text books when studying the following flow chart: Also use the animation on the SciWeb website under the Lecture – Neurology section

Summary Outline

I. Divisions of the Brain
 A. Higher Brain (Forebrain, Cerebral cortex)
   1. Rhinencephalon: Limbic system - allocortex (hippocampus, mammillary bodies, basal ganglia, thalamus, hypothalamus, olfactory bulbs, etc.)
   2. Neocortex: occipital, parietal, frontal and temporal lobes
     a. Cerebral hemispheres
     b. Cerebral cortex (outer gray matter)
 B. Lower Brain and Cerebellum
   1. Diencephalon (Interbrain)
     a. Thalamus
     b. Hypothalamus
   2. Brain stem
     a. Midbrain
       i. Cerebral peduncles
       ii. Corpora quadrigemina
       iii. Cerebellum
     b. Hindbrain
       i. Pons
       ii. Medulla
   3. Basal Ganglia
     a. Striatum: caudate nucleus and putamen
     b. Globus pallidus, claustrum, amygdaloid nucleus

II. Development and Growth
 A. Derived from ectoderm and develops from a region called the neural plate
 B. Neural plate develops into neural tube
 C. Anterior portion of neural tube develops into brain, posterior portion becomes the spinal cord
 D. Cavity of neural tube persists as ventricles of the brain and central canal of the spinal cord
 E. At cephalic end of neural tube, formation of three primary brain vesicles forerunners of forebrain, midbrain, and hindbrain
 F. Via process of flexures; growth of cerebral hemispheres over diencephalon, midbrain, and cerebellum; formation of sulci and gyri, brain assuming its final form

III. Cerebral Hemispheres

A. Description
1. Two cerebral hemispheres connected by corpus callosum, referred to as cerebrum
2. Cerebrum, largest part of brain, fills upper portion of skull
3. Surface composed of layer of gray matter called cortex
4. Beneath gray matter is white matter
5. Types of fibers in white matter
   a. Projection
   b. Association
   c. Commissural

B. Surface of cerebral hemispheres
1. Fissures
2. Sulci
3. Convolutions
4. Fissures
   a. Longitudinal
   b. Transverse
   c. Central sulcus, or fissure of Rolando
   d. Lateral cerebral, or fissure of Sylvius

C. Functions
1. Lobes
   a. Frontal
   b. Parietal
   c. Occipital
   d. Temporal
   e. Insula, or island of Rei
2. Governs all mental activities
   a. Organ of associative memory
   b. Reason
   c. Intelligence
   d. Will
   e. Seat of consciousness
   f. Interpreter of sensations
   g. Instigator of voluntary acts
   h. Exerts a controlling force on reflex acts
   i. Sleep-necessary for recovery of neurons
3. Motor area
      In front of central sulcus
4. Sensory Areas
   a. Behind the central sulcus
   b. Visual-occipital lobe
   c. Auditory-superior part of the temporal lobe
   d. Olfactory
   e. Gustatory-anterior part of temporal lobe
5. Association areas-cerebral tissue surrounding motor and sensory areas; interconnect and integrate motor and sensory areas.

IV. Limbic System (Rhinencephalon)
A. Rhinencephalon means olfactory brain; anatomically represented by olfactory bulb and tract, and areas of cerebral hemispheres involved with olfactory impulses
B. Rhinencephalon and connections with amygdala, thalamus, hypothalamus, and midbrain also involved with behavioral and emotional expression; term *limbic system* is used to define these functions

V. Basal Ganglia (Basal nuclei)
A. Masses of gray matter located deep within cerebral hemispheres, associated with lateral ventricles
   1. Caudate nucleus
   2. Lentiform nucleus
   3. Amygdaloid nuclear complex
B. Related both anatomically in location and functionally with the internal capsule
C. <u>Function</u>-involved in somatic motor functions

VI. Thalamus
A. Bilateral oval structures above midbrain, forms wall of third ventricle
B. Made up of many nuclei, each concerned with a specific function
C. Receives all sensory information with exception of olfaction

VII. Hypothalamus
A. Associated with third ventricle
B. Composed of many nuclei, each with specific function
C. Functions Autonomic nervous control
   1. Cardiovascular regulation
   2. Temperature regulation
   3. Food intake
   4. Water balance
   5. Gastrointestinal activity
   6. Sleep-waking activity
   7. Emotions

VIII. Midbrain
A. Short, constricted portion connects pons and cerebellum with the hemispheres of the cerebrum
B. Pair of cerebral peduncles
C. Consists of
   1. The corpora quadrigemina
   2. The cerebral aqueduct
D. Contains nuclei of the III and IV cranial nerves

IX. Cerebellum
A. Oval, constricted in center
B. Central portion called vermis
C. Lateral portions called cerebellar hemispheres
D. Gray matter on exterior
E. White matter in interior
F. Connected with cerebrum by superior peduncles
G. Connected with pons by middle peduncles
H. Connected with medulla by inferior peduncles
I. Function
   a. Participates in the coordination and integration of posture
   b. Coordinates the integration of posture and all voluntary skeletal muscle movements

X. Pons
A. Description
   1. Situated between the midbrain and the medulla oblongata.
   2. Consists of interlaced transverse and longitudinal white fibers mixed with gray matter
   3. Connects two halves of cerebellum and also medulla with cerebrum
B. Function
   1. Contains nuclei of trigeminal, abducens, facial, and vestibulocochlear nerves
   2. Participates in the regulation of respiration

XI. Medulla Oblongata
A. Description
   1. Pyramid-shaped mass, upward continuation of cord. Sensory and motor tracts of spinal cord represented. Many of them cross from one side to the other in the medulla; some end in medulla
   2. Gray matter forms nuclei
   3. Centers in which cranial nerves arise, centers for control of bodily functions
   4. Nuclei serve as Relay stations for sensory tracts to brain
B. Vital Centers
   1. Cardiac center
   2. Vasoconstrictor center
   3. Respiratory center
   4. Sneezing
C. Function - Controls reflex activities of
   1. Coughing
   2. Vomiting
   3. Winking
   4. Movement and secretions along the digestive tract

XII. Reticular Formation (reticular activation systemoRAS)
A. Description
   1. Network of interlacing cells and fibers
   2. Extends from upper spinal cord to diencephalon
B. Function
   1. Alerts cortex to wakefulness
   2. Sends efferent impulses to higher and lower centers

XIII. The Meninges (Coverings of the Brain)
A. Dura mater
B. Arachnoid mater
C. Pia mater

IVX. Blood Supply
A. Toward the Brain (arteries)
   1. Internal carotid Artery
   2. Vertebral artery
B. Away from the Brain (veins)
   1. Internal Jugular Vein
   2. External Jugular Vein

VX. Cranial Nerves

A. 12 pairs that emerge from various inferior parts of the brain and pass through foramina of the skull to innervate parts of the head and trunk

B. Classified as motor, sensory, and mixed nerves

C. The Twelve Cranial nerves (number, name, type)

Figure 14 Cranial nerves

I	Olfactory	Sensory	Sense of smell
II	Optic	Sensory	Vision
III	Oculomotor	Motor	Eye movements, dilation and constriction of pupil
IV	Trochlear	Motor	Eye movements
V	Trigeminal	Mixed	Chewing movements; sensation of head and face
VI	Abducens	Motor	Lateral eye movements
VII	Facial	Mixed	Facial muscle movements, saliva secretion; taste from front of tongue
VIII	Acoustic	Sensory	Hearing and upright balance
IX	Glossopharyngeal	Mixed	Swallowing, secretion, of saliva; taste; aid in reflex control of blood pressure and respiration.
X	Vagus	Mixed	Movements and sensation of heart, lungs, digestive organs, larynx
XI	Spinal Accessory	Motor	Movement of head, shoulder, larynx
XII	Hypoglossal	Motor	Movement of the tongue

XVI. Sensation-Interpreted in brain; may be modified or ignored

A. Tactile Sense

  1. Touch receptors-free nerve endings, hair nerve endings,

   a. Meissner's, pacinian corpuscles; all rapidly adapting except possibly free nerve endings

   b. Pressure different from touch; wide range of degree of pressure sensed

B. Kinesthesia

  1. Identifies location of parts of body, movement of parts

  2. Receptors located in joints, ligaments, joint capsules, pacinian,

  3. Ruffini end organs, Golgi end organs

C. Temperature

  1. Warmth-Ruffini end organs; cold-Krause end organ

  2. Range of temperature: 12 degrees through 50 degrees C; above this or below, pain results

  3. Adaptation occurs but incompletely

  4. Receptor is free nerve ending

  5. Stimulus is tissue damage, excessive heat or cold, inadequate blood supply, spasm of muscle, stretch of tubes

D. Pain

  1. Headache due to external head muscle spasm, stretching of meninges, dilation of brain blood vessels

  2. Referred pain is visceral pain that is referred to the skin area supplied with nerve fibers from same spinal segment

  3. Function of pain is protective

  4. Normal gastric hunger due to contractions of empty stomach, acting on nerves distributed to mucous membrane, and to hypothalamic centers

E. Hunger

Hunger contractions may be frequent and severe, even when food is taken regularly.

Multiple Choice

1. Vital centers of the medulla include those for control of:
   a. respiration, vomiting, heart rate
   b. respiration, hear rate, blood pressure
   c. respiration, sneezing, coughing
   d. heart rate, blood pressure, swallowing

2. The pons contains:
   a. a respiratory center
   b. the cerebellar peduncles
   c. the 5th through 8th cranial nerve nuclei
   d. all of the above

3. All of these are functions of the hypothalamus EXCEPT
   a. control of body temperature
   b. release of regulating factors that affect release or inhibition of other hormones
   c. principal relay station for sensory impulses
   d. center for mind-over-body (psychosomatic) phenomena
   e. involved in maintaining sleeping or waking state

4. The major function of the thalamus is to:
   a. relay sensory impulses to the cerebrum
   b. interpret sensations
   c. alert the organism
   d. control homeostasis

5. The hypothalamus is called a homeostatic center because it:
   a. responds to sensory input
   b. controls muscular activity
   c. lies beneath the cerebrum
   d. controls many processes essential for survival of the organism

6. The cerebellum:
   a. coordinates muscular activity
   b. integrates movements
   c. predicts when to stop movements
   d. all of the above

7. The primary somatic motor area of the cerebrum lies in the:
   a. frontal lobe
   b. parietal lobe
   c. occipital lobe
   d. temporal lobe

8. The primary somatic sensory area is found in the:
   a. frontal lobe
   b. parietal lobe
   c. occipital lobe
   d. temporal lobe

9. Association areas are those in which:
   a. specific motor areas are found
   b. specific sensory areas are found
   c. memories are stored, behavior is controlled, input is analyzed
   d. muscle tons is determined

10. The basal ganglion that most consistently shows damage in Parkinson's disease is the:
    a. globus pallidus
    b. putamen
    c. caudate nucleus
    d. substantia nigra

11. Epilepsy is characterized by:
    a. loss of consciousness
    b. a recurring pattern of seizures
    c. a lesion in the brain
    d. an "aura" before the seizure occurs

12. The arteries supplying most of the blood to the brain are the:
    a. basilar and vertebral
    b. internal carotid and vertebral
    c. Circle of Willis
    d. cerebral arteries

13. The blood-brain barrier refers to the fact that:
    a. some substances pass with difficulty through cerebral capillaries
    b. the brain is enclosed by the meninges
    c. Glia surround neurons
    d. there are no basement membranes in the cerebral capillaries

14. A "stroke" can result from:
    a. blocking of a cerebral vessel (e.g., clot)
    b. narrowing of cerebral vessel (e.g., atherosclerosis)
    c. Weakened and rupture of a cerebral vessel
    d. all of the above

15. Cerebrospinal fluid is produced by:
    a. choroid plexuses
    b. arachnoid granulations
    c. villi
    d. valves

16. Which of the following is not a function of cerebrospinal fluid?
    a. shock absorbing
    b. keeping cranial volume constant
    c. cooling the brain
    d. transporting solutes

| True and False |

1. _____ The post-central gyrus contains the primary somatic motor area.
2. _____ The reticular formation extends through nearly all brain stem.
3. _____ Midline stimulation of the precentral gyrus causes muscular movement on the lower limb.
4. _____ When the brain "comes to attention," alpha waves are interrupted.
5. _____ The thalamus may interpret the sense of pain.
6. _____ The visual area lies in the temporal lobe.
7. _____ The cerebellum operates at the conscious level.
8. _____ Each point on the body has a corresponding point in the thalamus and cerebrum.
9. _____ The hearing area lies in the temporal lobe.
10. _____ The cerebral peduncles carry sensory impulses to the cerebrum.
11. _____ The brain is very sensitive to deprivation of blood supply.

12. _____ The dural sinuses are arterial structures.
13. _____ Three main blood vessels run lengthwise on the cord.
14. _____ Glia lie very close to neurons, perhaps covering them.
15. _____ "Stroke" is a leading cause of death in the US.
16. _____ Loss of consciousness is a primary symptom of a CVA.
17. _____ CSF is found inside the spinal cord, as it is in the brain.
18. _____ CSF is formed by active and passive processes.

Completion

1. Apneustic breathing may result from damage to the:

2. Intense sensations of pain may result from damage to the:

3. Three homeostatic functions of the hypothalamus are:

4. The major cranial nerve of the autonomic system is the:

5. If one reaches for an object, and overshoots it, damage to the _____ is likely.

6. Three factors that aid in creating the "blood-brain barrier" are:

7. The ventricles and channels of the brain, in their order, that CSF flows through are:

_____ Pyramids

_____ Gracile and cuneate nuclei

_____ Pneumotaxic center

_____ Corpora quadrigemina

_____ Thalamus

_____ Arbor vitae

_____ l-dopa

_____ Diencephalon

_____ Ataxia

_____ Basal ganglia

_____ Prefrontal association area

_____ Limbic system

_____ Pyramidal system

_____ Alpha waves

_____ Jacksonian waves

_____ Purely sensory cranial nerves

_____ Oculomotor, trochlear

_____ Facial, glossopharyngeal

a. Used to treat Parkinson's disease

b. Concerned with emotions and emotional
    expression

c. Midbrain structures integrating auditory and
    visual reflexes

d. Occur in children and during emotional stress

e. Uncoordinated walking movements

f. Olfactory, optic, vestibulocochlear nerves

g. Formed by crossing of voluntary motor
    pathways

h. "Involuntary" motor system

i. Concerned with personality traits

j. Major sensory relay center

k. Cranial nerves serving sense of taste

l. Consists of thalamus and hypothalamus

m. Characteristic of an awake but relaxed brain

n. Nerve cells in medulla for synapses of touch
    pathways

o. "Voluntary" motor system

p. Tree-like white matter of cerebellum

q. Epilepsy associated with a brain lesion and
    abducens nerves

r. Area in pons controlling pattern of nerves
    breathing

s. Cranial nerves controlling eye movement

Matching Group 2

_____ Circle of Willis

_____ Hydrocephalus

_____ Cerebral aqueduct

_____ CVA

_____ Pneumoencephalogram

_____ Atherosclerosis

_____ Aneurysm

_____ Ventricle

_____ Subarachnoid space

_____ Arachnoid villus

a. Cerebral vascular accident

b. A thin-walled dilation of a blood vessel

c. Replacement of CSF by air in the brain followed by
    X-ray

d. Permits flow of blood between the two arterial
    supplies of brain

e. Contains CSF around brain and cord

f. Fatty deposition in blood vessel walls

g. Enlargement of the brain due to excess CSF

h. A hollow chamber; brain or heart

i. Site of absorption of CSF from subarachnoid space

j. Canal in midbrain connecting third and fourth
    ventricles

ANSWERS

Multiple Choice
1. b 2. d 3. c 4. a 5. d 6. d 7. a 8. b 9. c 10. d 11. b 12. b 13. a 14. d 15. a 16. c

True and False
1. false, 2. true, 3. true, 4. true, 5. true, 6. false, 7. false, 8. true, 9. true, 10. false, 11. true, 12. false, 13. true, 14. true, 15. true, 16. false, 17. false, 18. true

Completion
1. pons
2. thalamus
3. temperature regulation, water balance, control of pituitary function, etc.
4. Vagus
5. cerebellum
6. no pores in the capillaries, continuous basement membrane, covering of neurons by glia.
7. lateral ventricles, interventricular foramen, third ventricles, cerebral aqueduct, fourth ventricle

Matching Group 1
G, N, R, C, J, P, A L, E, H, I, B, O, M, Q, F, S, K
Matching Group 2
D, G, J, A, C, F, B, H, E, I

Figure 15 The effects of various drugs on the CNS

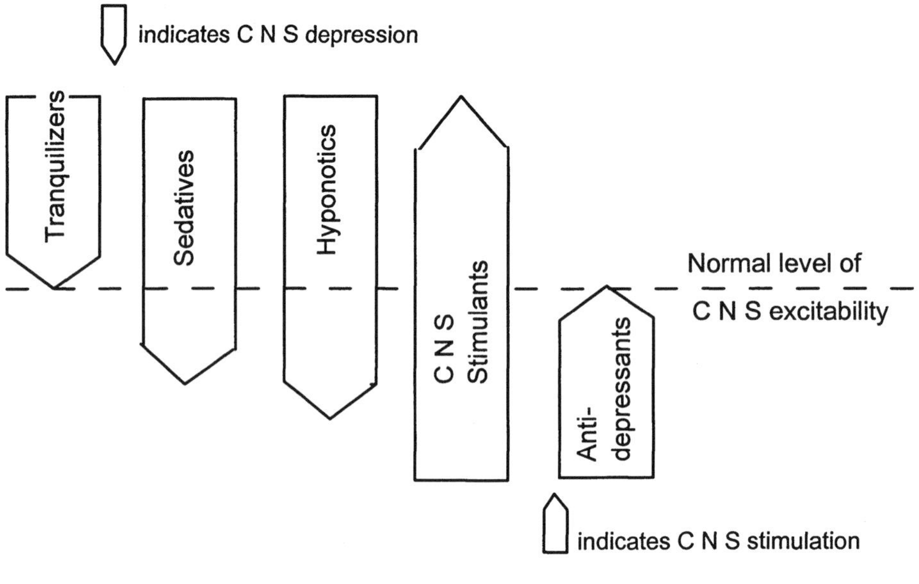

Sensory pathways
&
the Somatic nervous system

Chapter Objectives

1. Identify the principal sensory and motor pathways.
2. Compare the components, processes, and functions of the various motor pathways.
3. Explain how we can distinguish among sensations that originate in different areas of the body.
4. Describe the levels of information processing involved in motor control.
5. Discuss how the brain integrates sensory information and coordinates responses.
6. Explain how memories are created, stored, and recalled.
7. Distinguish between the levels of consciousness and unconsciousness, and identify the characteristics of brain activity associated with the different levels of sleep.
8. Describe drug-related alterations in brain function.
9. Summarize the effects of aging on the nervous system.

Concepts and Definitions

1. The perception sequence of a sensation requires a stimulus, a receptor, impulse conduction to the brain, and the translation of an impulse into a sensation within the cerebral cortex.
2. Sensations are characterized by projection, adaptation, after images, and modality.
3. Areas on and within the cerebrum constitute association areas that relate to emotional expression, personality, learning, memory, understanding of spoken and written words, and other facets of intelligence.
4. On the basis of location, receptors are classified as exteroceptors, visceroceptors, and proprioceptors.
5. The conscious cutaneous sensations include touch, pressure, cold, heat, and pain.
6. The waking state is believed to be maintained by the reticular activation system [RAS] within the midbrain and the cerebral cortex.
7. Sleep occurs in stages, and is a normal interruption of the waking state. Coma is a non-interruptable sleep indicated by suppression of neuron function. This could be the result of drugs and acidosis, or damage to neurons as by trauma, stroke, or infections.
8. Specialized pain receptors are found in practically every tissue of the body. Types of pain include somatic, visceral, referred, and phantom.
9. Substance P is involved with generating impulses related to pain along pain pathways. Endorphins exert their analgesic effects by inhibiting the release of substance P or by interrupting sensory impulses that pass through the opiate receptors of the thalamus on their way to cerebral cortex.
10. Pain impulses can also be inhibited by acupuncture in which needles are inserted through selected areas of the skin and then rotated. This concept is based on the Yin-Yang (Chinese cosmology) view of life within the Orient
11. Proprioceptive sensations provide people with a sense of position of body parts resulting from the degree of skeletal muscle contraction.

12. Sensory information transmitted from the spinal cord to the brain is conducted along two general pathways: the posterior column pathway and the spinothalamic pathway.

13. Voluntary skeletal muscle motor impulses are conveyed from the brain and into the spinal cord by way of two major pathways: the *pyramidal pathway* and the *extrapyramidal pathway* .

14. The integrative functions within the brain include cerebral activities such as memory, sleep, wakefulness, and emotions.

15. Emotion is a term that identifies four aspects of a situation: 1-cognition, 2-expression, 3-experience, and 4-excitement.

16. The limbic system is involved in the expression of emotions.

17. Memory is of three types: momentary, short term, and long term. The first two may be due to temporary neural pathways The third from the production of a protein to form a permanent neural pathway.

18. Electrical activity can be recorded from the brain on an electroencephalogram (EEG). Four basic types of EEG waves are seen, and represent the continuous activity of the brain.

19. Deviation from the normal EEG patterns is seen during seizure states, in brain injury, and often during the taking of certain drugs.

---

1. Which of the following is not a function of the cerebrum during an emotional response?
   a. cognition
   b. expression
   c. experience
   d. excitement

2. Stimulation of one of the following areas is followed by aggressive behavior:
   a. subcortical nuclei
   b. fornix
   c. hypothalamus
   d. amygdaloid nuclei

3. Directed emotional expression requires the:
   a. cortex
   b. amygdaloid nuclei
   c. hypothalamus
   d. fornix

4. Which of the following emotions is present in a newborn?
   a. fear
   b. comfort-discomfort reactions
   c. rage
   d. guilt

5. Learning may occur in the:
   a. spinal cord
   b. cortex
   c. synapses
   d. all of the above

6. Which of the following types of memory is believed to depend upon the formation of a protein?
   a. momentary
   b. long term
   c. short term
   d. none of the above

7. Electroshock or electroconvulsive therapy results in "destruction" of:
   a. long term memory
   b. learning
   c. short term memory
   d. RNA

8. Drugs that accelerate learning do so by:
   a. speeding consolidation of the memory trace
   b. increasing (stimulating) general nervous activity
   c. increasing RNA synthesis
   d. all of the above

9. Defective sensory perception may be produced by a lesion in the:
   a. frontal lobe
   b. parietal lobe
   c. occipital lobe
   d. temporal lobe

10. Disorders of memory and understanding are most commonly associated with lesions in the:
    a. frontal lobe
    b. parietal lobe
    c. occipital lobe
    d. temporal lobe

11. An EEG measures:
    a. electrical activity of the heart
    b. electrical activity of the brain
    c. electrical activity of muscles
    d. none of the above

12. A "brain wave" characteristic of the awakened but relaxed and inattentive brain is the:
    a. alpha wave
    b. delta wave
    c. beta wave
    d. theta wave

13. Evoked electrical activity:
    a. is associated with sensory stimulation
    b. appears in a brain area where sensory pathways for a sensation terminate
    c. can lead to learning and memory storage
    d. all of the above

14. A type of epilepsy that causes a "blank" in behavior is:
    a. psychomotor
    b. grand mal
    c. petit mal
    d. infantile spasm

15. The waking state of the organism is maintained by:
    a. a positive feedback system between reticular formation and cerebral cortex
    b. sensory input to the thalamus
    c. activation of the vital centers of the medulla
    d. exciting thoughts

16. REM sleep:
    a. is cyclical in nature
    b. is associated with dreaming
    c. is associated with acceleration of body activity
    d. all of the above

17. For a coma to develop, there must be involvement of the:
    a. cerebral cortex
    b. cerebellum
    c. brain stem
    d. spinal cord

18. Personality, social sense, and general intelligence is located in:
    a. frontal lobe
    b. parietal lobe
    c. occipital lobe
    d. temporal lobe

1._____ The cortex is responsible for directed emotional expression
2._____ The limbic system includes the cortex.
3._____ The limbic system does not include areas that give pleasurable sensations.
4._____ Fear and guilt are learned emotions.
5._____ Conditioning is a form of learning.
6._____ There are physical or anatomical changes that occur as learning proceeds.
7._____ Long term memory is most likely achieved by impulses circling over neuronal chains.
8._____ If short term memory is due to electrical impulses, electroshock therapy should wipe it out.
9._____ There are drugs that accelerate learning.
10. _____ Memories are stored in the temporal lobes.
11._____ Alpha waves are interrupted when attention is directed at something.
12._____ Delta waves always indicate brain abnormality.
13._____ An occasional seizure episode indicates the presence of epilepsy.
14._____ The upper portion of the reticular formation is concerned with arousal.
15._____ Sleep spindles in the EEG occur in stage 4 sleep.
16._____ Sleep deprivation alters normal behavior.
17._____ Coma involves the brain stem.
18._____ One's sense of values resides in the frontal lobes.
19._____ Most memories are stored in the parietal lobes.
20. _____ Parietal lobe lesions in association areas produce a failure to recognize familiar objects.

Completion

1. The four major brain areas comprising the limbic system are:

2. Destroying the amygdaloid nuclei, produces _____ in an animal. Thus, their integrity is essential for _____ .
3. A child will achieve a full set of emotional expressions by about _____ years of age.
4. Pavlov's dogs exhibited a form of learning called _____ .
5. Caffeine, amphetamines, and nicotine can speed learning because they are

_____ .
6. An _____ is a record of the continuous electrical activity of the brain.
7. A recurring pattern of seizure activity in the brain may lead to a diagnosis of

_____ .
8. A type of epilepsy in which seizures may be shown to have an organic or chemical cause is termed _____ epilepsy.
9. _____ is a term used to refer to an inability to comprehend written or spoken ideas.

Matching

GROUP 1

_____ Cognition

_____ Limbic system

_____ Preferred neuronal pathway

_____ Hippocampus

_____ Expression

_____ RNAase

_____ Emotion

_____ Newborn emotions

_____ Experience

_____ Protein synthesis

_____ Electrical impulses

_____ Excitement

A. Weighing an incident against previous experience

B. Destruction of RNA inhibits long-term memory

C. Repeated use of neuron chains causes enlargement of synapses

D. Momentary and short-term memory

E. Perception and evaluation of a stimulus

F. Comfort-discomfort, startle reaction

G. Essential for emotional expression

H. A reaction to an external or internal stimulus

I. External sign of emotion

J. Long-term memory

K. Storage area for recent memories

L. Vividness of the emotion

GROUP 2

_____ Alpha waves

_____ Beta waves

_____ Theta waves

_____ Grand mal seizure

_____ Reticular activating

_____ Stage 4 sleep

_____ REM sleep

_____ Coma

_____ Prefrontal association areas

_____ Temporal association areas

A. EEG waves seen in children and during emotional stress

B. The deepest, oblivious, stage of sleep

C. A state of unconsciousness with no response to strong stimuli

D. "Slow waves" in EEG when brain is inattentive

E. Lesions cause agnosia, apraxia, aphasia system

F. A seizure resulting in loss of consciousness

G. Lesions cause hyperactivity, personality changes

H. Waves of EEG when it is attentive

I. Modified stage 1 sleep, with dreams

J. The upper reticular formation and pathways to thalamus and cortex

ANSWERS

Multiple Choice
1.b 2.d 3.a 4.b 5.d 6.b 7.c 8.d 9.b 10.b 11.b 12.a 13.d 14.c 15.a 16.d 17.c 18.a

True and False
1. true 2. false 3. false 4. true 5. true 6. true 7. false 8. true 9. true
10. false 11. true 12. false 13. false 14. true 15. false 16. true 17. true
18. true 19. false 20. true

Completion
1. a) amygdaloid nuclei, b) hypothalamus, c) fornix, d) subcortical nuclei
2. passiveness, aggressive behavior
3. two
4. conditioning
5. stimulants
6. electroencephalogram
7. epilepsy
8. symptomatic or Jacksonian
9. aphasia

Matching
    GROUP 1
E, G, C, K, I, B, H, F, A, J, D, L

    GROUP 2
D, H, A, F, J, B, I, C, G, E

Autonomic nervous system
&
Higher order functions

Chapter Objectives

1. Compare the organization of the autonomic nervous system with the somatic nervous system.
2. Contrast the structures and functions of the sympathetic and parasympathetic divisions of the autonomic nervous system.
3. Describe the mechanisms of neurotransmitter release in the autonomic nervous system.
4. Compare the effects of the various autonomic neurotransmitters on target organs and tissues.
5. Discuss the relationship between the two divisions of the autonomic nervous system and the significance of dual innervation.
6. Explain the importance of autonomic tone.
7. Describe the hierarchy of interacting levels of control in the autonomic nervous system.

Concepts and Definitions

1.   The autonomic nervous system controls the activities of smooth muscle, cardiac muscle, and glands.
2.   The autonomic nervous system includes sensory (visceral afferents) and motor fibers (visceral efferents) that sense and regulate organs. The system operates involuntarily at the reflex level.
3.   The two divisions of the autonomic system are: the parasympathetic (craniosacral) portion, consisting of cranial nerves III, VII, IX, X the S2, S3 and S4 sacral spinal nerves, and the sympathetic (thoracolumbar) portion, composed of all thoracic and lumbar spinal nerves.
4.   Most body organs are dual innervated by fibers from both divisions. The parasympathetic conserves body resources and maintains normal function and responsible for "rest and relaxation". The sympathetic increases utilization of body resources and energy to prepare the body for "fight-or-flight."
5.   In general, sympathetic responses are primarily concerned with expending energy while increasing the activity of all systems excluding the urinary and digestive which it tends to inhibit.
6.   In general, parasympathetic responses are concerned with activities that restore and conserve energy by inhibiting all systems except for urinary and digestive which it tends to increase activities.
7.   Autonomic motor (efferent) fibers, like other axons throughout the nervous system, release chemical neurotransmitters at synapses as well as at synapses between post-ganglionic autonomic fibers and their visceral effectors of the neuromuscular junctions.
8.   On the basis of the chemical transmitter produced, autonomic fibers may be classified as either *cholinergic* or *adrenergic*.
9.   The preganglionic neurons at the ganglia of both the sympathetic and parasympathetic division use acetylcholine and the enzyme, AChase. The postganglionic neuron of the sympathetic secretes epinephrine and/or norepinephrine, and causes (according to the chemical secreted) different effects on the organ (usually excitatory activity). Agents that block the effects of norepinephrine (called beta-blockers) are often used to treat hypertension and some cardiac disorders.

10. The preganglionic bodies of the sympathetic division are located in spinal segments T1 to L2. The sympathetic ganglia, which contain the cells bodies of the postganglionic neurons lie close to the spinal column along the vertebral bodies in the rami communicants. These ganglia and the connecting nerves are called the paravertebral chain or sympathetic trunk and chain ganglia.

11. The major neurotransmitter released by the postganglionic fibers of the sympathetic division is norepinephrine (NE) <u>NOT</u> epinephrine. Most adrenaline (epinephrine) is released by the adrenal medulla.

12. The preganglionic cell bodies of the parasympathetic nervous system (PNS) are located in the brain stem and the sacral spinal segments (S2 to S4). The parasympathetic ganglia are located in or near the structures they innervate. Acetylcholine is the neurotransmitter released at both pre- and postganglionic nerve endings of the parasympathetic nervous system.

13. Biofeedback is a process in which people get constant signals, or feedback, on visceral body functions such as blood pressure, heart rate, and muscle tension.

14. Synapses between preganglionic and postganglionic neurons occur in ganglia or plexuses that lie by the spinal cord (vertebral ganglia) or peripherally (collateral ganglia).

15. Yoga is defined as a higher consciousness achieved through a fully rested and relaxed body and a fully awake and relaxed mind.

Summary Outline

I. ANATOMY OF THE AUTONOMIC NERVOUS SYSTEM

A. Sympathetic Nervous System (Thoracolumbar)
1. Preganglionic neurons (cells of origin) in the lateral horn gray of the spinal cord (intermediolateral cell column) from the C-8 to L-2 or L-3.
2. Cholinergic fibers
3. Three different organizations of the sympathetic ganglia
  a. -Paravertebral ganglia - chain of 22 ganglia on each side of the spinal cord connected together forming the sympathetic chain
  b. -Prevertebral or collateral ganglia - these lie in the thorax, abdomen and pelvis anterior surface and proximity to the Aorta and its abdominal branches.
  c. -Terminal or peripheral ganglia - small collections of ganglia located in close proximity to the innervated organ
4. Post ganglionic neurons (cells of termination)
  a. Originate in one of the above ganglia and terminate at the effector organ
  b. Most fibers are adrenergic
5. Four great plexuses
  a. Cardiac plexus
  b. Celiac plexus
  c. Hypogastric plexus
  d. Solar plexus
B. Parasympathetic Nervous system (Craniosacral)
1. Ganglia located close to innervated organ, often in wall of organ
2. Preganglionic neurons (cells of origin) located at one of three levels within the CNS
3. All preganglionic fibers are cholinergic fibers
  a. . midbrain (also called tectal outflow) - cells originate in Edinger Westphal autonomic nerve giving rise to autonomic fibers carried by the III cranial nerve (oculomotor) to the ciliary ganglion. These terminate at the circular muscles of the iris thus responsible for pupillary reflexes.

b. Medullary outflow - Autonomic fibers leave the brainstem in the VII (facial), IX (glossopharyngeal), and X (Vagus) nerves
    i. Facial nerve innervates lacrimal, nasal, sublingual and submaxillary glands.
    ii. Glossopharyngeal nerve innervates parotid gland
    iii. Vagus nerve parasympathetic control to most body organs. This nerve transmits 80% of all parasympathetic impulses
c. . Sacral Outflow - Preganglionic neurons (cells of origin) - located in the ventral horn of the gray matter at the S-1, 2, 3 and 4 spinal nerves. These fibers exit the ventral root and travel with a spinal nerve to the organ. These innervate the organs of the inferior abdomen and most of the pelvic cavity
4. Postganglionic fibers (cells of termination) - These are extremely short
5. Most postganglionic fibers are cholinergic.

II. FUNCTIONS OF THE ANS
A. Governs the homeostasis of all innervated organs
B. Parasympathetic Division (rest and relaxation division)
    Increases the activity of the Urinary and Digestive systems and inhibits or reduces the activity of all other systems.
C. Sympathetic Division (fight or flight division)
    Increases the activity of all systems except for the Urinary and Digestive which it inhibits or reduces.
D. Most important function is to mediate many visceral reflexes such as blood pressure, digestion, etc.

E. Ganglia function as relay stations for impulses to the viscera.
    1. Nicotine paralyzes the autonomic ganglia.
    2. Many of the viscera are supplied with nerves from both divisions - functions of these two sets are often antagonistic.
    3. Norepinephrine is the mediator for postganglionic sympathetic nerve endings (adrenergic fibers), except fibers to sweat glands (cholinergic fibers).
    4. Acetylcholine is the mediator for most parasympathetic postganglionic nerve endings (cholinergic) and all preganglionic sympathetic and parasympathetic fibers.

III. CONTROL OR REGULATION OF THE ANS
A. Subcortical Regulation of Parasympathetic and Sympathetic Activities
B. Hypothalamus is the control center for the major functions of the ANS.
C. The sympathetic and parasympathetic nervous systems complement (antagonize) each other in the regulation of the body's visceral processes.
D. The system is augmented (aided or assisted) by hormones of the adrenal medulla.

Figure 16 Comparison of sympathetic to parasympathetic systems, table

Characteristics	Sympathetic Nervous System	Parasympathetic Nervous System
Origin	Thoracolumbar spinal nerves Lateral horns of spinal cord	Craniosacral spinal nerves Brain stem for cranial nerves Spinal cord for sacral nerves
Innervates	Abdominal viscera Sweat glands Cardiac muscle Blood vessels Smooth muscle	Abdominal viscera Glands Cardiac muscle Smooth muscle
Structural Neurons	Preganglionic fibers Postganglionic fibers Multipolar shape	Preganglionic fibers Postganglionic fibers Multipolar shape
Locations of preganglionic neurons	Lateral horn gray of spinal cord from C-8 to L-2 or L-3 Terminates in Paravertebral ganglia Collateral ganglia Terminal or peripheral ganglia (see below)	
Length of neuron	Preganglionic - long Postganglionic - long	Preganglionic - long Postganglionic - short
Extent of neural control	Extensive and non specific	Specific and distinct
Autonomic ganglia	Interconnected as 1-chain ganglia (vertebral ganglia) and 2-collateral ganglia (prevertebral ganglia)	Individual and non connected Often in wall of organ
Location of ganglia	1-chain ganglia are interconnected and adjacent to vertebral column 2-collateral ganglia (also called prevertebral ganglia) and close to organs 3-terminal ganglia	Terminal ganglia are adjacent to or on effector organs
Overall effects	Increases the activity of all systems EXCEPT urinary and digestive which it inhibits	Decreases the activity of all systems EXCEPT urinary and digestive which it increases or excites
Homeostasis	Decreases healing Dominates during stress response Energy consumptive "Fight or Flight" activity Reduces immunity Antagonizes parasympathetic Easier of two systems to stimulate	Increases healing Subdued during stress Energy productive an saving "Rest and Relaxation" activity Increases immunity Antagonizes sympathetic More difficult of two to stimulate
Sensory Pathways	Visceral (or splanchnic) afferents are rare if any	Visceral (splanchnic) afferents are infrequent and inaccurate
Motor pathways	Visceral (splanchnic) efferents dominate	Visceral efferents dominate
Neural locations	Pre ganglionic and post ganglionic neurons	Pre ganglionic and post ganglionic neurons
Pharmacology (intrinsic)	Preganglionic is cholinergic Postganglionic mainly adrenergic with a few cholinergic (urinary and digestive)	Preganglionic is cholinergic Postganglionic mainly cholinergic with a Few adrenergic (urinary and digestive)
Pharmacology (extrinsic)	Stimulated by: cocaine, amphetamines, adrenaline Depressed by: ergot (a mold on the Rye plant)	Stimulated by: acetylcholine Depressed by: atropine

1. The autonomic system:
   a. operates by reflexes
   b. contains visceral afferent and efferent fibers
   c. contains ganglia and plexuses
   d. all of the above

2. The parasympathetic system:
   a. contains nerves from the brain and thoracic cord
   b. contains nerves from the brain and sacral cord
   c. contains nerves from the thoracic and lumbar cord
   d. none of the above

3. Parasympathetic effects:
   a. prepare the body to resist stress
   b. lead to acceleration of body activity
   c. maintain normality of body function
   d. cause rage and emotional reactions

4. There are autonomic controlling centers in:
   a. cerebral cortex
   b. hypothalamus
   c. medulla
   d. all of the above

5. Drugs may be used to treat autonomic disorders. They may act by:
   a. preventing synaptic transmission
   b. stimulating the sympathetic system
   c. stimulating the parasympathetic system
   d. combinations of the above

| True and False |

1. _____ Body viscera are innervated by both divisions of the autonomic system.
2. _____ The parasympathetic system increases energy expenditure.
3. _____ Postganglionic cell bodies lie in the periphery.
4. _____ Autonomic activity never reaches the conscious level.
5. _____ Sympathetic stimulation results in more widespread response than does parasympathetic stimulation.
6. _____ The Vagus nerve is an autonomic nerve.
7. _____ Most sympathetic postganglionic neurons are adrenergic.
8. _____ Parasympathetic post ganglionic fibers secrete acetylcholine.
9. _____ Acceleration of heart rate is a parasympathetic effect.
10. _____ The adrenal medulla, smooth muscle of blood vessels in skin, and sweat glands have parasympathetic nerves.

1. The autonomic nervous system consists of 2 groups of fibers called:

2. Outgoing autonomic fibers leave the spinal nerve complex by way of the:

3. Three autonomic outflows of fibers occur from the:

4. Organs not receiving parasympathetic fibers include:

Matching

    _____ Preganglionic neuron   a. Continuous
    _____ Sympathetic ganglia   b. High blood pressure
    _____ Craniosacral   c. Synonym for parasympathetic
    _____ Sympathomimetic   d. Autonomic neuron from CNS to synapse in a ganglion
    _____ Tonic effect   e. Synonym for sympathetic division
    _____ Postganglionic neuron   f. A substance having the same effect as stimulation of the
                                     sympathetic nervous system
    _____ Thoracolumbar   g. Removal of sympathetic ganglia
    _____ Parasympathomimetic   h. Receive preganglionic neurons from thoracic and lumbar cord
    _____ Hypertension   i. Substance mimicking effects of parasympathetic stimulation
    _____ Sympathectomy   j. Autonomic neuron from synapse in a ganglion, to effector

ANSWERS

Multiple Choice

1. d 2. b 3. c 4. d 5. d

True and False

1. true 2. false 3. true 4. false 5. true 6. true 7. true 8. true 9. false 10. false

Completion

1. visceral afferents, visceral efferents   2. white rami 3. brain, thoracic and lumbar cord, sacral cord   4. sweat glands, blood vessels of skin

Matching

D, H, C, F, A, J, E, I, B, G

Index